Praise for *Who Says Yo*

"Intriguing scenarios to test your intellect and stimulate intense (possibly violent) debate among family and friends. It's a medical mashup of *Dr. Strangelove*, *House*, *Gattaca*, and *Mindwalk*. Fascinating stuff."
—CAROLYN JOURDAN, author of *Medicine Men*

"*Who Says You're Dead?* is an invitation to engage in serious conversation with yourself and your world about how to walk an ethical path in life. This book challenged and excited me, and it will you too."
—CARL A. HAMMERSCHLAG, author of *The Dancing Healers*

"The topics in this book challenge our notions of the fractal boundaries of life and death, right and wrong, and our place on the long road of human progress."
—CLIFF A. PICKOVER, editor of *The Science Book*

"Dr. Appel doesn't tell you what to think, but he guides you in how to think about some of the most pressing issues in healthcare."
—JEFFREY L. SEGLIN, author of *The Good, the Bad, and Your Business*

"To practice medicine is to live with ethical dilemmas. Dr. Appel shows why these quandaries often have no simple answer, only difficult choices."
—MICHAEL FOSSEL, author of *Cells, Aging, and Human Disease*

"This is a highly useful and illuminating collection for clinicians, teachers, patients, families, and students of medical ethics."
—SUSAN ONTHANK MATES, author of *The Good Doctor*

"Highly engaging." **—DAVID J. HELLERSTEIN, MD, Professor of Clinical Psychiatry, Columbia University, and author of *Heal Your Brain***

"Marvelously instructive and engaging. Pondering these ethical dilemmas could almost be considered a primer on how to think critically."
—STEPHEN R. BOWN, author of *Island of the Blue Foxes*

"Dr. Appel gives concise background on each case, but not necessarily the answers. This book offers opportunities to think about reconciling the clash of human values behind the clinic and hospital room doors."
—SALLY SATEL, coauthor with Scott O. Lilienfeld of *Brainwashed*

"There is a tremendous breadth of knowledge demonstrated here, gained from years of considering the Solomonaic answers to difficult moral questions."
—HUDSON OWEN, author of *Hospital Days*

"In this comprehensive, serious, often funny, and above all inviting book, Dr. Appel brings a scholar's eye, a humanist's heart, and a physician's experience to the real world, practical ethics of the bedside."
—FRANK HUYLER, author of *The Laws of Invisible Things*

"One could not ask for a more comprehensive, readable, or enjoyable review of current bioethical concepts."
—PHILIP A. MACKOWIAK, MD, author of *Diagnosing Giants*

"This book is full of awful dilemmas in bioethics, of the sort that would make a medical student blanch and a layperson pray for deliverance. It's a lot of fun to read."—JEANETTE KEITH, author of *Fever Season*

"From the classroom to the clinic to the dinner table and even to social media, all might engage with Dr. Appel's hard choices and the challenges that they pose to one's moral compass." —HARRY OSTRER, MD, author of *Legacy*

"An impressively researched collection of real-life issues many of us will face. Read now and prepare yourself."
—TOM HARBIN, MD, MBA, *The Business Side of Medicine*

"Today's moral frictions and complexities are imbued with copious empathy for multiple points of view. I recommend *Who Says You're Dead?* without reservation." —HARRIET A. WASHINGTON, author of *Infectious Madness*

"Dr. Appel provides a view of moral matters in medicine that speaks to his many years in medicine's clinical trenches. Each of these 101 conundrums is described and analyzed with clarity and insight."
—JONATHAN B. IMBER, author of *Trusting Doctors*

"A page-turner for the thoughtfully curious reader. Dr. Appel asks us to look beyond the life or death decisions, and instead, ask ourselves: Can we live with the ethical choices we make?"
—MOLLY CALDWELL CROSBY, author of *Asleep*

"*Who Says You're Dead?* entertains as it educates. It is an exotic journey, and strongly recommended."
—E. FULLER TORREY, author of *Evolving Brains, Emerging Gods*

Who Says You're Dead?

—✠—

Medical & Ethical Dilemmas for the Curious & Concerned

JACOB M. APPEL, MD

ALGONQUIN BOOKS OF CHAPEL HILL   2019

Published by
ALGONQUIN BOOKS OF CHAPEL HILL
Post Office Box 2225
Chapel Hill, North Carolina 27515-2225

a division of
Workman Publishing
225 Varick Street
New York, New York 10014

Published simultaneously in Canada by Thomas Allen & Son Limited.

Design by Steve Godwin.

Library of Congress Cataloging-in-Publication Data

[TK]

10 9 8 7 6 5 4 3 2 1

First Edition

In memory of Professor Edward Beiser,
who asked all the hard questions,
and for Rosalie, who helps me find the answers

The names of the doctors in the hypothetical dilemma portions of this book are drawn from literature, film, television, and even comics. They are all fictional; any resemblance to real medical professionals, living or dead, is entirely coincidental. No connection is intended between the fictional doctor and the material described in the dilemma.

CONTENTS

Part Five: Practical Matters

INTRODUCTION

—∾∾—

Today's hospitals and clinics are the settings of some of the most challenging and controversial ethical dilemmas our society confronts. Every day, it seems, a pioneering researcher or clinician announces a new breakthrough: hand transplants, cloned sheep, targeted biological cancer therapies, cognitive enhancers, preimplantation genetic screening, transgenic mice—the list of scientific "miracles" seems endless. With these technologies, of course, arise far more complex moral challenges. How to allocate scarce donor hearts and kidneys among potential recipients, for example, is not an issue unless the immunosuppressive drugs that prevent our bodies from rejecting those organs exist. Now they do.

Two recent technological developments offer windows into the strikingly different sorts of ethical challenges that such advances pose. One of these innovations is three-parent conception. As readers may or may not recall from high school biology, most of our DNA is housed in the nuclei of our cells, but some of our genetic blueprint is contained in small organelles outside the nucleus called mitochondria. Both types of

DNA are necessary to produce a healthy baby. Under rare circumstances, the DNA in the mitochondria becomes defective through mutations; as a result, babies are born with debilitating genetic diseases. These conditions often run in families. To prevent these diseases, doctors can now take the nucleus of an egg cell from a potential mother who comes from such a family and can combine it with the mitochondrial DNA of a second, unrelated woman. This process is known as "cytoplasmic transfer." If this combined egg is then fertilized by a sperm, the result will be a baby with DNA from three distinct biological parents—what the media has dubbed a "three-parent baby." On the one hand, this is a great breakthrough: women once faced with the choice of conceiving a sick child or no child at all can now give birth to healthy offspring who live long, meaningful lives. On the other hand, such a process raises novel questions: Should two mothers be listed on this child's birth certificate? What happens if the woman who contributed mitochondria demands partial custody? Visitation rights? An inheritance? Alternatively, does the child ever have a right to learn the identity of the mitochondrial donor? Or the donor's medical history? And in the age of surrogate motherhood, if the embryo is implanted inside a third woman's uterus, what are the ethical and legal implications for a "four-parent baby"? While more than a dozen babies have been born over the past two decades through cytoplasmic transfer, many of these questions remain unresolved.

At the opposite end of the technological spectrum stands an advance far more familiar to the average healthcare consumer: the rise of the electronic medical record (EMR). These days, anyone who visits a doctor's office or hospital emergency room has likely encountered the ubiquitous appearance of the computerized chart. Experts tell us that these EMRs will decrease medical errors and speed the transfer of health information. The ultimate goal, for many, is a so-called "intraoperative system," where a patient can walk into any hospital or physician's office in the nation, and the staff will immediately be able to access the patient's medical history, current medications, and regular healthcare providers' contact information. This technology might prove particularly valuable in emergencies or when a patient has lost consciousness.

At the same time, it is fraught with the potential for lost privacy. Millions of healthcare professionals would require access to such a system for it to function well. But some patients may not want their records available in this manner. They may object to their podiatrist knowing that they suffer from a mental illness or their dentist learning what method of contraception they use. The potential for abuse also remains glaring: How will the system know if a pharmacist from Wyoming accesses the medical records of his soon-to-be son-in-law in Florida in order to discover whether his daughter will be marrying a man with a history of drug addiction? And if he does breach the system in this way, how should we punish him? Firing the victim's future father-in-law may actually exacerbate the injured man's misfortune and will certainly not put the genie back in the bottle. And then, of course, there is the possibility that hackers will break into the system and post the medical records of everyone on the internet. Certainly, these pitfalls require a careful balancing between privacy rights and access to top-notch care.

As a practicing psychiatrist and bioethicist, I explore these exciting and often daunting ethical dilemmas every day. Over the course of nearly two decades teaching at Brown University, Columbia University, New York University, and the Icahn School of Medicine at Mount Sinai, I have written a trove of these difficult conundrums to stimulate discussion among medical students and residents. Some are drawn from the headlines, others loosely modeled on cases reported in professional journals. A few, painstakingly disguised, come from my own clinical encounters. Whether you are planning a career in healthcare or you are a layperson intrigued by the ethical issues you often witness all too briefly on popular television shows, the dilemmas that follow are designed to let you investigate your own values, engage with difficult "real-world" issues, and argue (in good cheer) with friends and family across the dinner table.

The commentary provided after each conundrum is not intended to sway your opinions. Rather, these are reflections that offer some of the real ways in which established bioethicists, clinicians, and policy makers have tackled similar moral quandaries. Some of these quandaries may arise in your own life, and there is value in having thought about the issues in advance. The hope is that you will examine these questions from multiple vantage points, whatever your ultimate feelings, and will recognize that intelligent people of goodwill may arrive at different conclusions.

In the hospital or in the legislature, addressing these highly fraught subjects can prove emotionally grueling. Fortunately, discussing them hypothetically, in your own living room, should be precisely the opposite: invigorating and inspiring. Above all, the goal of this volume is to convey the intellectual pleasure of engaging with complex ethical questions—to let you do what professional bioethicists do every day. So I do hope you enjoy!

JACOB M. APPEL, MD, JD, MPHIL, MPH, MFA
Director of Ethics Education in Psychiatry
Assistant Professor of Psychiatry and Medical Education
The Mount Sinai School of Medicine

Who
Says
You're
Dead?

PART ONE

Inside the Mind
of a Doctor

T he ethical norms of the physician-patient relationship have evolved considerably since the Hippocratic oath of ancient Greece forbid doctors from performing surgery. As late as the nineteenth century, many medical practitioners questioned the value of empirical evidence and offered remedies grounded in unproven theories—including bloodletting, purgatives, and toxic metals like mercury and arsenic. The effective arsenal of the medical practitioner was limited: citrus for scurvy, iodine for goiters, inoculation for smallpox. Encounters with physicians often did more harm than good. Although some states attempted to rein in the profession, beginning with the passage of New York's Medical Practices Act in 1806, credentialing standards proved extremely lax. By 1860, the United States had one physician for every 571 people—by far the highest rate in the world.

Over the next century, the American Medical Association (AMA) and various other professional societies played an instrumental role in reshaping healthcare into one of the nation's most heavily regulated fields. Doctors are now licensed, and their numbers are strictly limited; many medications require a prescription. An age of scientific discovery and rapid advances in technology, including the ongoing genetic revolution, have helped to realize cures that seemed unfathomable only a generation ago. How doctors should use this newfound power remains one of the central ethical challenges of the twenty-first century.

1

"You're Not My Real Dad"

FRED IS A seventy-five-year-old widower who suffers from kidney failure and faces a lifetime on dialysis. After a lengthy discussion with his longtime physician, Dr. Arrowsmith, Fred decides to seek a potential kidney donor among his friends and family members. His only daughter, Linda, who is nearly fifty, agrees to be tested to see whether she is an appropriate match.

The results of the ensuing tests shock Dr. Arrowsmith. Not only is Linda not a match, but genetic markers reveal that Linda cannot be Fred's biological daughter. In other words, Fred's late wife likely had an extramarital relationship that led to Linda's conception.

Should Dr. Arrowsmith tell either father or daughter of this discovery?

REFLECTION: False Paternity

MISATTRIBUTED PATERNITY, COMMONLY known as false paternity, is not an uncommon phenomenon. Estimates suggest that 1.7–3.3 percent of children are mistaken regarding the identities of their biological father. This occurrence has significant implications well beyond healthcare. For example, a staple of junior high school science classes once was having students perform ABO (Landsteiner) blood typing on themselves and then comparing their blood types to those reported by their parents. One can imagine the family discord such an exercise might create if parents and children display biologically incompatible results.

On the one hand, if Dr. Arrowsmith decides to reveal Linda's false paternity, the consequences may prove psychologically devastating for both father and daughter. On the other hand, concealing the information has significant healthcare implications as well. For example, Linda may believe both of her parents to be Scandinavian. If she has children of her own, she may forgo genetic testing for diseases not frequently found among Scandinavians, such as Tay-Sachs disease, a deadly childhood illness that is most common among eastern European Jews, French Canadians, and Louisiana Cajuns. But if Linda's biological father were not Scandinavian, her own offspring might still be at risk. Not knowing her authentic family history could lead to preventable diseases in her own children. Linda might also unwittingly report an incorrect family history to her doctors, who could then underestimate her risk of everything from early-onset colon cancer to suicide. One can also imagine a different case where the daughter is found not to be a biological child but is still a potential match as a kidney donor. Under those circumstances, sharing the false paternity results might deter the daughter from donating a kidney and thus prove medically compromising to the potential recipient.

Ethicist Barron Lerner once described a case similar to this one in a New York Times column. In that case, which occurred at the University of Toronto, the doctors chose to disclose the discovery, which the family—after initial "shock and distress"—was able to accept. The patient's daughter reported being grateful to learn of the misattributed paternity from the medical staff, rather than later, under different circumstances. Other families might respond with less equanimity. How hospitals should handle these cases of unexpected nonpaternity remains controversial. Some hospitals now have patients and family members sign disclaimers prior to organ-transplant compatibility testing, which specifically state that discoveries of false paternity resulting from the testing will not be disclosed, while others continue to believe that they have an ethical obligation to share such discoveries.

2

"How Many of Your Patients Survive?"

Dr. Dolittle is the chief of neurosurgery at a well-respected community hospital. A retired couple, Bonnie and Stan, arrive at the emergency room. Stan is complaining of the worst headache of his life—and a brain scan reveals he is suffering from an aneurysm that requires surgery within twelve to twenty-four hours or he will likely die. Bonnie asks Dr. Dolittle what the success rate is for the surgery, and he tells her, truthfully, that 60 percent of his patients survive the procedure. Dr. Dolittle knows that at a hospital twenty minutes away by ambulance, another doctor, Dr. Quincy, has a surgical survival rate of 85 percent.

Should Dr. Dolittle volunteer this information to Stan and Bonnie?

REFLECTION: Informed Consent

Informed consent is one of the foundations of modern Western medicine. In order for patients to make meaningful decisions about their healthcare, they have to know the potential risks and benefits of each of these decisions. In fact, being able to state the risks and benefits of a given medical intervention is one of the requirements for determining whether a patient is mentally sound enough to make his own choices. At the same time, physicians are not expected to outline all of the risks of a particular intervention. For example, during an appendectomy, it is theoretically possible that a patient might fall off the operating table, hit her head, and suffer brain damage—but the chances are rather remote, so this is not a part of the standard informed consent for the procedure.

The truth is that, with regard to cognitively intact patients, "informed consent" is actually a misnomer. It does not matter whether the patient actually understood enough to consent meaningfully; what matters is that the physician provided sufficient information for a "reasonable" or ordinary person to have understood the risks and benefits. Some plastic surgeons even record their informed consent process on video, so that in cases of alleged malpractice they can prove to a jury precisely what they said. Why such an objective "reasonable person" yardstick? Because a subjective approach (i.e., one that asks whether this particular patient actually understood the risks) would open the door to second-guessing and even outright perjury by the patient at a future malpractice trial. Hindsight is twenty-twenty. Football fans understand how easy it is to play Monday morning quarterback. Unfortunately, even with rigorous standards, informed consent often fails to serve patients' needs. Medical historian David Rothman reported in 2006 that "anywhere from 25 to 50 percent of patients and subjects do not understand what they have agreed to."

Physicians are generally not expected to share the success rates of other providers—although there might be an exception at the extremes: a physician who has never performed the operation before, for instance, might be expected to reveal this information to a patient. However, society generally places the burden on the patient to "shop around" or to get a second opinion. If Bonnie had asked Dr. Dolittle directly whether other physicians could perform the aneurysm repair better, he would be wrong to lie point-blank, but he could probably get away with simply telling her that he cannot speak for the success rates of other providers.

One should note that an alternative rule, which would compel physicians to share their comparative success rates, might have the unintended consequence of steering traffic toward a handful of first-rate providers. Over time, fewer surgeons would master the technique for aneurysm repair, and overall access to quality care might be reduced. Success rates can also reflect the patient population served, so compelling surgeons to share their outcome data might lead them to cherry-pick their patients—making it more difficult for the sickest patients to find providers. Finally, in many cases, sharing such information would help only wealthy patients: If a patient lives in poverty in a housing project in New York City, being told that the success rate for treating a particular condition is better at the Mayo Clinic in Minnesota may not prove very helpful. If the patient cannot get to the Mayo Clinic, this knowledge will not help him medically, and could harm him psychologically.

3

"Please Don't Tell Anyone about My Crime"

DURING A ROUTINE session with his longtime psychiatrist, Dr. Sarah Cooper, thirty-five-year old Marcel confesses to a crime from his college years: While arguing with a neighbor, Olivia, over loud music, he lost his temper and shoved her. Olivia fell down Marcel's kitchen staircase and broke her neck—dying instantly. Marcel panicked and buried the body in a state park many hours away. When pressed by Dr. Cooper, he reveals the precise location. The body has never been found, and Olivia remains listed as a missing person.

Dr. Cooper believes Marcel, who is now happily married and has two young children, when he swears the death was accidental. Marcel is unwilling, however, under any circumstances, to convey this information to the authorities. He forbids Dr. Cooper from doing so as well.

Dr. Cooper looks up the case on the internet and discovers that Olivia's parents continue to hold out hope that she remains alive. Each year, they record a video plea for her safe return that is broadcast on the local television station. Dr. Cooper realizes that merely informing the family or the authorities anonymously that Olivia is dead will not resolve their uncertainty and will perhaps raise even more questions. Yet she fears that notifying them of the location of the body might lead them to forensic evidence that will incriminate Marcel.

Should Dr. Cooper reveal the location of Olivia's body to the woman's family and/or the police?

REFLECTION: Doctor-Patient Confidentiality

Confidentiality is essential to the relationship between physicians and patients. Reliance on confidentiality proves especially significant in patient interactions with mental health professionals, such as psychiatrists and psychologists. If a patient is unwilling to speak candidly with his psychiatrist for fear of disclosure, the result may be misdiagnosis or inappropriate treatment. These general principles are enshrined in the Health Insurance Portability and Accountability Act of 1996, better known as HIPAA, but they date back to the Hippocratic oath and many other professional creeds. Although federal law and professional guidelines generally leave some limited opening for breaching confidentially in pursuit of the general welfare, even these exceptions have narrowed in recent years. In the landmark case of Jaffee v. Redmond (1996), the US Supreme Court established a "psychotherapist-patient privilege," which generally affords patients the right to prevent their psychiatrists and psychologists from testifying against them in court. In fact, the protections from psychiatrist-patient confidentiality are generally much stronger and broader than those that apply to other physicians.

Many states follow what is known as "the Tarasoff rule," which not only allows, but requires, psychiatrists (and often other mental health professionals) to breach confidentiality to warn and protect potential victims of future crimes. At least one state, Iowa, in a high-profile arson case, extended this duty to include the protection of private property. A 1994 study by Marcus J. Goldman and Thomas C. Gutheil revealed that many psychiatrists believe a similar legal duty exists to report past crimes, but this is not the case. In fact, doing so under some circumstances opens the psychiatrist up to malpractice liability. The Principles of Medical Ethics of the American Psychiatric Association (APA) limit the permissibility of such breaches to situations in which the psychiatrist is protecting the community from "imminent danger." These circumstances might include, arguably, a case where an innocent third party has been convicted of the patient's prior crime.

At least one leading psychiatric ethicist, Paul Appelbaum, has raised the possibility that the exception might also apply when the victim is suffering substantially as a result of the patient's failure to confess. It is not much of a stretch to apply a similar exception in the case of Marcel and Olivia, when the victim's family appears to be suffering. However, such breaches run the risk of causing larger damage: mental health patients may then hold back information about past criminal acts whose disclosure is vital to their treatment. Such well-founded mistrust would damage the patients' own well-being without any clear benefit to their victims or their victims' families—as psychiatrists would never hear many patient confessions at all.

4

"Please Don't Put It in My Chart"

CARRIE IS A twenty-five-year-old woman who lives with a violent male partner, Charles. She arrives at the emergency room of her local community hospital with a black eye and a broken wrist. After some coaxing, she tells the physician on duty, Dr. Zira, that her partner is responsible for her injuries. Dr. Zira documents this in the medical record.

Several hours later, once her wrist has been cast and she is ready for discharge, Carrie summons Dr. Zira back to her bedside. "Please don't put anything in my chart about Charles hurting me," she says. "He has friends who work at this hospital. If they find out what I told you, it will get back to him and he'll hurt me again."

There is an "override" in the hospital's electronic medical record (EMR) system to remove information that is both inaccurate and could be dangerous (such as a wrong blood type) from a patient's chart.

Should Dr. Zira use this method to remove this accurate information from Carrie's chart?

〜〜〜

REFLECTION: Privacy and Medical Records

PRIOR TO THE 1970s, many healthcare professionals looked askance at anyone requesting access to their own medical records—fearing that patients would generally fail to understand the contents. Concerns over litigation, the loss of medical mystique, and convenience likely played a role in such secrecy as well. Since 1996, HIPAA has guaranteed patients the right to view their medical charts within thirty days. Many state laws require even more immediate access. The federal statute also gives patients the opportunity to append a "statement of disagreement" to their medical record if they object to any of its contents. Such statements may prove of value when there is a genuine dispute over facts. Yet in cases where the patient's concerns are for privacy, rather than accuracy, such a statement is of little value. As a general rule, hospitals limit employee access to medical records to individuals directly involved in a patient's care. However, policing access can prove challenging, especially in the era of EMRs, and enforcement often occurs only after the fact. Firing a worker who illegally accessed and shared private information may prove little comfort to a patient whose secrets have already been divulged.

In Carrie's scenario, she appears to have sincere concerns for her personal safety; she is frightened that her partner's friends may access her records without authority and reveal the contents to him. She may also fear that the secrets she related to Dr. Zira could be used against Charles in court—which is likely permissible in certain states and under federal evidence rules. Many hospitals allow celebrity patients, and others with compelling needs, to register under aliases. Some rogue hospital employees have learned this fact the hard way, when they have illegally accessed the charts of famous patients—like Bill Clinton or Farrah Fawcett—only to discover that they have accessed "fake" records instead. It is not clear whether Dr. Zira's hospital offers such an option to patients like Carrie, or if it did, whether doing so would genuinely protect her from the staff members whom she fears. Few, if any, hospitals allow patients to opt out of the EMR entirely, and all physicians are required by law to keep records of patient encounters. In fact, failure to keep an adequate medical record is grounds for losing one's license in many states.

The purpose of the medical record is to be accurate and comprehensive, because a more complete record will lead to better patient care. One can imagine other patients requesting that providers delete information related to drug use, mental health diagnoses, or reproductive services from their records— but also the serious consequences that might result from such willful omissions. Not knowing that a patient takes psychiatric medications, for instance, might lead an emergency room physician to prescribe an incompatible remedy that could prove lethal. While physicians are wise to display some discretion in what they document, such as excluding a gratuitous insult that the patient offers about his mother-in-law, there are significant consequences to excluding medically pertinent data. In Carrie's case, one can easily envision her, at a future date, needing evidence of her partner's conduct in a custody battle or when seeking an order of protection. Or she might show up at the hospital unconscious with worse injuries the following week, and not knowing her abuse history, the staff might leave her with Charles unsupervised—affording him an opportunity to hurt her again. Unfortunately, either honoring or refusing Carrie's request might pose a significant future risk to her well-being.

5

When the President Has a Secret

A RETIRED PSYCHIATRIST, Dr. Eckleburg, recalls treating one of the major party nominees for US president, now in his late fifties, when the psychiatrist was in training and the politician was in his early twenties. Dr. Eckleburg vividly remembers the case because the politician's father was a prominent elected official and the patient had attempted suicide. It was the patient's second suicide attempt, and he was diagnosed with manic depression (now better known as bipolar disorder). To Dr. Eckleburg's surprise, the candidate releases his "entire" medical record to the public as part of his campaign, and there is no mention of any suicide attempts, mental illness, or the psychiatric medications generally prescribed to prevent patients with bipolar disorder from relapsing.

Needless to say, Dr. Eckleburg is concerned that the future leader of the free world may have a serious untreated psychiatric illness, or that he is a liar. At the same time, he is reluctant to break the candidate's medical confidentiality, especially as he has not seen him in thirty years.

Should Dr. Eckleburg leak the politician's psychiatric history to the media?

REFLECTION: Public Disclosure

No LAW REQUIRES candidates for the presidency to release medical information to the public. In fact, for much of US history, the health of the occupants of the Oval Office was regarded as entirely a private matter. Significant medical conditions, some of them debilitating, remained concealed from voters. Historians say that Woodrow Wilson likely suffered strokes in 1896 and 1906, the latter of these six years before assuming the presidency and thirteen before a more severe stroke rendered him incapacitated for much of his final two years in office; Dwight Eisenhower struggled with Crohn's disease starting in his thirties; John F. Kennedy battled Addison's disease and chronic pain. A 2006 study by Duke University psychiatrist Jonathan Davidson and others suggests that eighteen US presidents between 1776 and 1974—49 percent—met the criteria for the diagnosis of a psychiatric disorder. While President Eisenhower did release some health information to the media, the health of political candidates first became a major national issue when Senator Thomas Eagleton of Missouri, the running mate of 1972 Democratic presidential nominee George McGovern, withdrew from the ticket after he admitted that he had undergone electroshock therapy for depression.

Over the last few decades, presidential candidates have released their medical records to varying degrees, most notably the extensive disclosure of medical records by Republican candidate John McCain in 2000 and 2008. Yet at least one serious contender for the presidency, Democratic candidate Paul Tsongas, overtly deceived the public when declaring himself cancer-free in 1992. In fact, a bone marrow transplant had failed to cure the non-Hodgkin's lymphoma, which ultimately killed the former senator in 1997.

Although, as noted previously, physicians generally have a fiduciary duty to protect the confidences of patients, no duties are truly absolute. Extraordinary circumstances may exist where the public safety or welfare requires a breach of such confidentiality. In the scenario posed, Dr. Eckleburg must decide whether the situation justifies such a breach—knowing that he may face professional and legal consequences.

A related set of questions arises regarding the medical secrets of deceased presidents. For instance, several US presidents have been rumored to have sired illegitimate children. The possibility that President Grover Cleveland fathered a boy, Oscar, with a woman named Maria Crofts Halpin made the chant "Ma, Ma, where's my pa?" a rallying cry of the 1884 election campaign. President Warren G. Harding's reputation was tarnished by the posthumous accusation, leveled by Nan Britton in The President's Daughter (1927), that the married Harding was the father of her daughter, Elizabeth Ann. For many years, surviving relatives of Harding disputed Britton's claim. However, DNA testing in 2015 firmly established a close genetic link between both sets of heirs, solving a long-standing historical mystery.

Not all interest in the DNA of historical figures relates to paternity. A prominent California cardiologist and medical historian, John Sotos, has made a plausible case that Abraham

Lincoln suffered from a rare genetic disorder, multiple endocrine neoplasia, type 2B. DNA testing on surviving Lincoln artifacts, such as the now-bloodstained cloak he wore to Ford's Theatre on the night of his assassination, might shed light on this hypothesis and might explain Lincoln's psychological state in the later years of his public service, but the owners of these artifacts have proven reluctant to permit such testing. Revealing the secrets of past presidents may clarify the historical record, but might also have an impact on living relatives—such as the discovery that the family might still carry a genetic disorder. Another factor in the ethics of revealing secrets related to deceased political leaders might be whether survivors knew the deceased figure personally or hold some other direct connection to him. As time passes, under this latter standard, the claims of survivors will become more tenuous.

While the specific ethical questions Dr. Eckleburg faces will arise rarely, the broader implications for public trust in physicians are significant. Few people will likely withhold confidences from their psychiatrists for fear that they will be used against them in a presidential run, but many patients outside the public eye might withhold information if they fear their secrets could be shared with others.

Individuals with bipolar disorder, when appropriately treated, can live extremely productive lives, and many such individuals hold high positions in the public sector. Rather than breach the candidate's confidentiality, another approach might be for Dr. Eckleburg to reach out to the candidate and his current physicians directly—to ascertain whether he is truly untreated or is merely deceiving the public about his treatment. If the candidate is untreated and dangerous, a reasonable case could then be advanced for revealing the diagnosis to the public. The argument for breaching confidentiality is far weaker if the candidate is merely lying, which, unfortunately, places him in the company of many other politicians.

6

"The Worst Patient Ever"

DR. MCKENNA RUNS a dialysis clinic. His clinic provides life-prolonging artificial kidney treatments to hundreds of patients each week. Most are very appreciative. Lucinda is the rare exception. She is, in the words of Dr. McKenna's head nurse, "the worst patient ever." Lucinda often appears at the clinic drunk, or high on cocaine. Even when she arrives clean and sober, she frequently hurls racist and anti-Semitic comments at the staff and at other patients. On several occasions, when she was upset, she pulled dialysis tubing out of the arm of the patient in the neighboring bed, so now she must receive treatment alone in the far corner of the clinic under the watch of a nursing assistant. She refuses a psychiatric referral, but she does not appear to Dr. McKenna to be mentally ill, merely an extremely unpleasant person. Still, multiple efforts by Dr. McKenna over two years have failed to achieve a working relationship with Lucinda.

One afternoon, when she feels the staff has kept her waiting for treatment too long, Lucinda topples several chairs in the waiting area and breaks a glass coffee table. Dr. McKenna has had enough; he decides that he will no longer provide treatment for Lucinda. However, with her history, it's possible that no other hospital or clinic will assume care for her. Without dialysis, she will eventually die.

Is it ethical for Dr. McKenna to give Lucinda notice that he will stop providing dialysis for her in six months, whether she can find another dialysis provider or not?

∿

REFLECTION: Patient Conduct

PHYSICIANS IN PRIVATE practice have broad latitude to choose which patients they treat, as long as they do not discriminate on the basis of protected statuses like race or religion. This freedom is subject to the criticism that physicians are generally sheltered from market forces by the government—through various mechanisms (e.g., limitations on medical-school class sizes and residency positions, retraining requirements for physicians educated abroad, etc.) that keep the number of doctors artificially low and, hence, fees artificially high. Having the talent to practice medicine is not enough to acquire a medical license or hang up a shingle; one must also meet lengthy and complex credentialing requirements designed to constrain entry into the field. Since doctors do not operate in a free market, but rather as part of a protected guild, some commentators argue they should have charitable service obligations connected to their licensure. However, no such mandates exist. This contrasts with the duty of hospitals, which under the Emergency Medical Treatment and Labor Act (EMTALA) of 1986, must stabilize every patient who comes through their doors.

Once a patient is already under the care of a particular physician, certain safeguards do exist to shield that patient from abandonment. As a general principle, a doctor can "fire" a patient as long as she affords the patient reasonable time and opportunity to find another provider. In psychiatry, for instance, six months is generally considered an ample interval to arrange alternative care. Usually, doing so is not difficult. Yet some patients, for a variety of reasons, will face practical challenges in managing such a transition. Sometimes, a patient's mental status or healthcare literacy will prove so limited that she cannot be expected to find a new provider on her own. A patient suffering from dementia, for example, should not be asked to seek a different neurologist unaided. Under such circumstances, the original provider may be expected to assist with the transfer of care.

A very small number of patients find no alternative options. In one high-profile 2009 case, Grady Memorial Hospital in Atlanta closed a dialysis clinic that served many undocumented immigrants who were ineligible for treatment elsewhere. The ensuing court battle saw some of these patients repatriate, others move to states with more lenient Medicaid policies, and a few rely on hospital emergency rooms for urgent dialysis. In California, a dialysis patient with severe addiction and behavioral problems, Brenda Payton, was "fired" by her dialysis clinic for unruly behavior, even though no other provider would accept her. A California appeals court ruled in favor of her doctors in 1982. While such a precedent is not legally binding outside of California, it may offer guidance to courts in other states.

Whatever Dr. McKenna ultimately decides about Lucinda, he can take comfort in knowing that courts and professional associations, while they generally look unfavorably upon doctors who abandon patients recklessly or for pecuniary gain, have historically been sympathetic in cases where a patient's conduct was both egregious and relentless.

7

"I'd Never Actually Do It, But . . ."

A NEW PATIENT, Danny, comes to Dr. Maturin, a family medicine physician, complaining that he is having trouble sleeping, is frequently agitated, and cannot concentrate at work. In explaining his symptoms to her, Danny starts to describe his sexual fantasies involving his seventeen-year-old stepdaughter. He reveals that he sometimes gets up at night and watches her as she sleeps. He also mentions that he daydreams about lying down next to her and fondling her breasts. "I don't think I'd actually do anything," says Danny. "I'm ninety-nine percent sure." He later says, "You won't tell anyone about my fantasies, will you? If my wife knew, she would leave me—and I do love her very much, even if I am unhappy with our sex life."

Doctors in Dr. Maturin's state are expected to report a "reasonable suspicion" of child abuse or neglect to the state's child welfare agency.

Should Dr. Maturin report Danny's conduct, knowing that the state will investigate and that Danny's wife will likely learn of his fantasies?

REFLECTION: A Doctor's Duty to Report

ALTHOUGH REPORTS OF child abuse have peppered medical literature as far back as the nineteenth century, the issue did not receive widespread attention among physicians until the publication of a groundbreaking paper, "Battered Child Syndrome," by pediatrician C. Henry Kempe, radiologist Frederic N. Silverman, and psychiatrist Brandt F. Steele in 1962. Their paper galvanized the public. By 1967, every state had passed a mandatory-reporting statute, requiring physicians to disclose suspected abuse. The federal government passed its own law, the Child Abuse Prevention and Treatment Act (CAPTA) in 1974, making state reporting requirements a prerequisite for certain federal funds. Many statutes require healthcare providers—and others involved in childcare, such as teachers and social workers—to report a reasonable suspicion of abuse or neglect, leaving to the state authorities the responsibility of determining whether mistreatment actually occurred. Such mandatory disclosure differs from rules regarding other forms of abuse. In some states, for example, physicians not only face no requirement to report spousal abuse, but they are prohibited from doing so. The reason advanced for this distinction is that battered adults can make their own decisions regarding the risks and benefits of reporting mistreatment, while children are not yet able to do so.

The definition of child abuse is clear at the extremes; on the cusp between abuse and discipline, however, a gray area exists. The public became privy to this liminal space in the controversy surrounding Minnesota Vikings running back Adrian Peterson, who faced criminal charges in 2014 for whipping his four-year-old son with a switch. The football star maintained that such punishment was within the community standard, but ultimately pled no contest to a misdemeanor assault charge. Corporal punishment remains legal in nineteen states, and in 2014 Deborah Kotz reported in the Boston Globe that as recently as 2012, "77 percent of men, and 65 percent of women agreed that a child sometimes needs a 'good hard spanking.'" Certain cultural practices can also be mistaken for abuse, including "cupping" and "coining"—alternative medical therapies that leave temporary marks on the skin. The challenge in potential child-abuse cases is that underreporting places children's lives in danger but overreporting runs the risk of significantly damaging innocent families. The investigation process, which often involves removing children from their parents' homes, is not benign.

Danny has placed Dr. Maturin in a difficult spot by revealing his fantasies. On the one hand, he has not yet acted on them—and may never do so. Dr. Maturin must decide whether the 1 percent chance that her patient reports that he might act on these fantasies at some hypothetical point in the future constitutes a "reasonable suspicion" of child abuse. If Dr. Maturin believes so, she must report Danny. Mandatory-reporting laws are per se rules, which afford no discretion. On the other hand, considerable subjectivity—and, hence, discretion—exists in determining whether Danny's behavior meets the "reasonable suspicion" standard. So despite mandatory-reporting laws, physicians often still find themselves bearing the weight of such no-win decision-making.

8

Sleeping with the Doctor

RITA IS A fifty-seven-year-old woman in outpatient therapy with a veteran psychiatrist, Dr. Stockmann. Rita is a shy and anxious divorcée who often describes herself as being "insignificant" or "worthless," and states that she has always been inhibited about sexual involvement. In fact, she reveals to Dr. Stockmann that she has had only one fulfilling romantic relationship in her entire life. Fifteen years ago, she had gone to a different out-patient psychiatrist, Dr. Praetorius, for treatment of her social anxiety. After a month of weekly therapy, Dr. Praetorius said to her: "I can't continue to treat you, because I find you too attractive. But I would love to start seeing you romantically." The pair then dated clandestinely for two years, until Dr. Praetorius broke off the relationship. Rita believes that he "fell in love" with another patient, although she cannot prove this. She has no regrets about her relationship with Dr. Praetorius, except that it ended, and demands that Dr. Stockmann not share her secret.

Sexual relationships between psychiatrists and patients or former patients are considered malpractice and often result in the physician losing his or her license. Dr. Praetorius was a leading psychiatrist in the community, but he has recently retired. He continues to serve on various committees and advisory boards, although he is no longer treating patients.

Should Dr. Stockmann report Rita's allegations to the state medical board, despite her insistence that he not do so?

〜〜〜

REFLECTION: Doctor-Patient Attraction

ETHICAL NORMS AND many state laws prohibit sexual relationships between healthcare providers and their patients. For instance, California bans marital and family therapists from having such relationships until two years after treatment has ceased. The American Psychological Association's Ethics Code similarly forbids relationships between psychologists and patients for at least two years after their last professional contact—and even then, such relationships are permitted only under the "most unusual circumstances" where the psychologist can establish that there has been no exploitation. The rules governing psychiatrists in the US are even more stringent: they may never have sexual relationships with people they have treated. States have refused to carve out exceptions, even for providers who marry patients long after treatment terminated. The argument for a blanket per se rule is that such relationships inherently "mismanage the transference" between doctor and patient—a fancy way of saying that, even after psychotherapy ceases, doctor and patient are never equals.

Rules governing psychiatrist-patient sex were far more fluid until the 1970s. Many prominent figures in the psychiatric field, including Carl Jung and Bruno Bettelheim, are alleged to have had affairs with their patients; a 1972 study by psychiatrist Sheldon H. Kardener found that 10 percent of Los Angeles psychiatrists admitted to sexual relations with individuals under their care. The American Psychiatric Association did not formally prohibit such relationships until 1973. Only with the case of Roy v. Hartogs in 1975 (later the basis for the NBC movie *Betrayal,* starring Rip Torn and Lesley Ann Warren) did the profession fully turn against doctors like Renatus Hartogs, who was accused of using his office as a pickup lounge. Yet such conduct persists: former APA president Jules Masserman was sued in the 1980s by four former patients for sexual misconduct; psychiatrist Jack Gorman, the president of Harvard's McLean Hospital, surrendered his license in 2007 following such an affair.

Most psychiatrists and ethicists now view therapist-patient sex as unethical—although some disagreement remains regarding relationships with former patients pursued after a lengthy passage of time. The issue of romantic relationships with the close relatives of patients has also become a concern, with at least one state medical board penalizing the practice. Most states require physicians to report knowledge of the misconduct of colleagues; much of the time, if one discovers a fellow psychiatrist is sleeping with a patient, one has a moral obligation to report that transgressor to the state. Yet the situation is more difficult in cases such as Rita's, where Dr. Stockmann has learned of the alleged conduct during the course of therapy, and where the patient is actively discouraging him from taking any action.

Physicians have considerable leeway in breaching confidentiality to prevent serious future dangers to the health or safety of others. If Dr. Praetorius were still treating patients, Stockmann might face a difficult task of determining whether protecting the public from his renegade colleague would justify the damage he might cause to his therapeutic relationship with Rita. As Dr. Praetorius is not actively engaged in patient care anymore, the risk to the public appears much lower. (Of course, Dr. Praetorius might still return to practice someday.) Under such circumstances, most—but not all—ethicists would argue against divulging Rita's secret. At the same time, Dr. Stockmann may wish to work with his patient to persuade her to take the matter to the licensing board on her own, an act which might both serve justice and prove therapeutic.

9

A Physician with a Dark Past

As AN EIGHTEEN-YEAR-OLD, Hugh became involved with a neo-Nazi street gang and eventually killed a member of a rival gang in a shoot-out. He was convicted of voluntary manslaughter and served three years of a fifteen-years-to-life sentence before a judge freed him on a technicality. During his time in prison, Hugh earned a GED; after his release, he worked his way through college and graduated with high honors in biology and physics. He is now twenty-seven and wants to become a physician. He takes the MCAT—the admissions test for medical schools—and receives nearly a perfect score. In his applications, he explains that he regrets his past actions and rejects any affiliation with white supremacism.

If not for his criminal past, Hugh would almost certainly gain admission to an excellent US medical school. While many states do not permit convicted felons to practice medicine, because Hugh committed his crimes prior to medical school admission, it is possible that a state would defer to the judgment of the medical-school admissions process in determining his eligibility to practice. If Hugh graduates from medical school, he may become a licensed physician.

Should Hugh be admitted to medical school despite his violent past?

REFLECTION: Professional Standards

SURVEYS CONSISTENTLY PLACE physicians among the most trusted and respected of professionals. This is true across many nations. Much of this respect derives from faith in the integrity of healthcare professionals. There is the old joke that 99 percent of lawyers give the other 1 percent a bad name; nobody says such things of doctors. In order to maintain such widespread trust, which is essential to the effective doctor-patient relationship, medical schools and licensing boards generally turn away candidates of questionable character. Since 2002, the Association of American Medical Colleges has required applicants to reveal felony arrests and convictions on their applications. It also recommends criminal background checks for all prospective students. Historically, "moral turpitude" has been the standard for striking physicians off the medical rolls. Yet one person's immorality may not be another's. Consensual homosexual conduct was once considered a crime of moral turpitude. In Arizona, a would-be lawyer who had failed to pay his school loans was turned away from the bar on these grounds.

The prospect of a murderer-turned-medic arose in Sweden in 2008, when Karl Helge Hampus Hellekant (later, a.k.a. Karl Svensson), a former neo-Nazi convicted of killing a prominent union activist in 1999, enrolled as a medical student at the Karolinska Institute. As a general policy, Swedish medical schools do not ask about prior criminal convictions, and Hellekant did not reveal this information on his application or during his interviews. He was later dismissed from the university on a technicality. However, his case prompted considerable soul-searching among medical gatekeepers, both in Sweden and around the world.

Many critics of Hellekant's admission questioned whether patients would trust a former killer. If not, did admitting him to a prestigious professional school—in place of another applicant—do a disservice to the public? And would allowing Hellekant to practice diminish overall trust in doctors? New York Times columnist Lawrence Altman reported that Harriet Wallberg-Henriksson, then the Karolinska's president, referred the case to the institute's ethics committee for guidance; among the questions she asked: "Must educators and administrators inform patients about a convicted criminal student's past?" Medical students, after all, interact extensively with patients during their training. Advocates for Hellekant noted that his distinctive experiences might render him uniquely fit to provide medical care to prisoners and ex-convicts, a historically underserved population.

If one excludes candidates like Hugh, in the scenario at the start of the chapter, from the practice of medicine, one must ask where one draws the line. Should financial fraud be a disqualifier? Drunk driving? Fishing without a license? The legal profession has confronted similar questions in several high-profile cases. Reginald Dwayne Betts, who served eight years in prison for a carjacking committed at age sixteen, later graduated from Yale Law School; the Connecticut Bar Examining Committee initially rejected his application for admission to the bar on grounds of moral "character and fitness" but ultimately relented, and he was admitted to the practice of law in 2017. This contrasts with the case of Stephen Glass, a former New Republic reporter who fabricated a series of feature stories and later applied for membership in the California bar. The California Supreme Court rejected his application; he subsequently found work as a paralegal.

Whatever the merits of allowing Hugh to practice medicine, such a decision is likely to prove unpopular, as the public generally expects physicians to manifest the highest ethical standards—possibly even higher than those they have come to expect of attorneys.

10

Turning a Blind Eye to Torture

DR. BANNER IS a military physician with the US Navy. He is informed by his superiors that "enhanced interrogation techniques" will be used upon several detainees who are allegedly suspected of terrorism. Some critics have labeled these techniques as torture.

The navy would prefer to have a physician available should any of the detainees suffer a medical emergency during the interrogation. "All you have to do is sit inside the officers' lounge and read the newspaper," says his commanding officer. "If we have an emergency, we'll call for you." Dr. Banner's superior officer also says that if the navy cannot find a doctor to be on hand for emergencies, the authorities will pursue the interrogations anyway without a physician available. "We won't force you to do it," says his boss, "but we'd strongly prefer it. Your country would strongly prefer it. And it is the right thing to do."

Is it ethical for Dr. Banner to participate in this interrogation process in the indirect manner requested by his superiors?

———— ∞ ————

REFLECTION: Enhanced Interrogation

THE CANONS OF medical ethics have long banned physicians from participating in torture. These proscriptions were explicitly laid out in the World Medical Association's Declaration of Tokyo (1975), the United Nations Principles of Medical Ethics (1982), and the United Nations Convention against Torture (1984). The American Medical Association Code of Medical Ethics goes one step further, noting that "physicians must not be present when torture is used or threatened." The AMA code also warns that "physicians may treat prisoners or detainees if doing so is in their best interest, but physicians should not treat individuals to verify their health so that torture can begin or continue."

Whether "enhanced interrogation techniques" used by the US military constitute torture has been a matter of considerable controversy. In preparing for the interrogation of detainees at Guantanamo Bay, Deputy Assistant Attorney General John Yoo and Assistant Attorney General Jay Bybee advised the Bush administration that such techniques did not constitute torture. Critics, such as Physicians for Human Rights, strongly disagree. While the AMA and the American Psychiatric Association forbid members from participating in enhanced interrogation, the American Psychological Association once sanctioned such engagement. Psychologists James Elmer Mitchell and Bruce Jessen allegedly participated in guiding the examination of al-Qaeda prisoners. They were later sued by the American Civil

Liberties Union on behalf of several of these detainees; the case was settled on terms that have not been publicly disclosed.

Dr. Banner is not being asked to participate directly in enhanced interrogations. Rather, he has been informed that such interrogation will occur with or without his presence; his sole role is to aid prisoners who suffer negative medical consequences. Yet some of those patients could theoretically be revived by him only to face more questioning. Under the circumstances, if these techniques are indeed torture, he is rendering assistance that might permit it to continue.

The scenario, in essence, asks how complicit one must be in unethical conduct before one suffers moral responsibility for that conduct. These same questions arise in a number of areas where physicians interface with law enforcement. For instance, now that most major medical organizations have prohibited physician participation in capital punishment, one must ask whether psychiatrists are permitted to certify that patients have the capacity to understand why they are being executed—a US Supreme Court requirement for such executions to go forward. Dr. Banner may legitimately feel he is helping these internees by making himself available to provide emergency care. However, he must balance those noble intentions against the harm he may do by lending his good name, and the good name of his profession, to legitimizing potentially unethical behavior.

11

When Medical Secrets
Are Business Secrets

Dr. Hawkeye Pierce is an oncologist with a "high-end" practice near New York's Wall Street. One of his patients, Herman, is being treated for a terminal brain tumor. Herman is also the CEO of a major US corporation. Recently, a larger US company has agreed to merge with that corporation. Under the publicly announced plan, Herman, considered a genius in his field, will run the combined company.

Health rumors swirl around Herman, who appears sickly and emaciated, but he publicly attributes this appearance to long-standing anemia. "Otherwise, I'm fit as an ox," Herman tells the media. "There is absolutely nothing else wrong with me. My doctors tell me I could live another fifty years." Herman's remarks drive both stock prices up more than 20 percent. Dr. Pierce is aware that Herman's remarks constitute fraudulent stock manipulation and might be illegal.

Should Dr. Pierce share his knowledge with the Securities and Exchange Commission?

∼∼∼

REFLECTION: CEO Responsibility

CONSIDERABLE VARIATION EXISTS regarding how much medical information US business leaders disclose to shareholders. At one extreme, Google cofounder Sergey Brin announced in 2008 that he carries a genetic mutation linked to Parkinson's disease, increasing his hypothetical risk of the disorder at a distant point in the future. At the opposite extreme, Apple cofounder Steve Jobs went to great lengths to conceal his treatment for the neuroendocrine tumor of the pancreas that ultimately killed him in 2011. Some high-profile executives have opted (as far as we know) for full and rapid disclosure of health issues: Harry J. Pearce of General Motors, Jamie Dimon of JPMorgan Chase, Berkshire Hathaway's Warren Buffett. In contrast, Kraft Foods initially refused to reveal the reasons behind then-CEO Roger Deromedi's medical leave in 2004, while Bear Stearns kept entirely silent about leader Jimmy Cayne's hospitalization for life-threatening sepsis in 2007.

Controversy exists over whether, and to what degree, grave illnesses among business luminaries must be reported to the Securities and Exchange Commission (SEC). Securities litigator Allan Horwich has argued that, at a minimum, under rule 10b-5.3 of the Securities Exchange Act of 1934, making a "deliberately false material statement about the health of a corporation's luminary" is unlawful; US courts have largely arrived at the same conclusion. While one can argue about the definitions of both "luminary" and "material," few would likely maintain that the declarations of Herman, the CEO dying of a brain tumor, have not crossed the statute's red line.

Yet the question in this scenario is not whether Herman has a legal duty to reveal his diagnosis to investors, but whether Dr. Pierce is ethically permitted to share that diagnosis with the SEC. Both the federal government, through HIPAA, and many states limit the grounds upon which physicians may breach doctor-patient confidentiality to those in which the patient's conduct poses "a serious and imminent threat to the health or safety of an individual or the public." Warning the probable victim of a violent crime, for instance, clearly falls under this exception; in fact, many states require doctors to attempt such a warning. Certain other exceptions are specified in federal law, such as those permitting doctors to report an escaped convict or a crime that occurs on their own premises. Barring such exceptions, physicians generally cannot breach confidentiality.

Whether a judge or jury would find Herman's dishonesty a serious threat to the public is uncertain but seems improbable. The fact that the confidential knowledge is medical in nature also favors maintaining confidentiality. However, one can envision cases involving large-scale financial fraud where providers breaching doctor-patient confidentiality might have a more compelling case—like a physician who might have turned in Ponzi schemer Bernie Madoff or the leadership of Enron. Interestingly, although state courts afford litigants a doctor-patient privilege, federal courts do not; if Herman is ultimately charged with a breach of securities law, Dr. Pierce may still be compelled to testify against him.

For the time being, society has decided that protecting trust between doctors and patients is, on the whole, more important than any social benefit to be gained by allowing breaches in cases of financial wrongdoing. So legally, Dr. Pierce's hands are likely tied. Whether they should be, especially in the context of the various financial frauds exposed over the past decade, is a more challenging question. Of course, Dr. Pierce is certainly free to use his persuasive talents to convince Herman to disclose the truth himself. Alternatively, as long as Herman is able to obtain adequate medical care elsewhere, Dr. Pierce has every right to refuse to continue to treat him while he is perpetrating a fraud on the public. Oh—and in case you are wondering, it would be both illegal and unethical for Dr. Pierce to short-sell stock in Herman's company.

12

A Doctor's Buried History

EMMA, A MEDICAL student, dabbles in historical research during her spare time. She is writing a paper on the Oakfield hepatitis experiments, a series of studies conducted at her state's hospital for mentally impaired children during the 1960s. The most disturbing of these experiments involved intentionally infecting the patients, many of them African American toddlers with IQs under 70, with viral hepatitis in order to study various potential treatments. While no children died, several became severely ill. At the time, the study was not considered objectionable by mainstream investigators, but it is now held up as an example of abusive and unethical research.

In the Oakfield archive, Emma discovers a document naming several college students who worked as volunteers on the experiment. One of them is now-seventy-five-year-old Dr. Van Helsing, her school's most preeminent physician, who has been a long and vocal advocate for patient welfare at the local hospital and for human rights around the world. Emma knows that revealing Dr. Van Helsing's role in the Oakfield experiments would tarnish his reputation significantly. At the same time, she is troubled that he has never revealed his part in this tragedy.

Should Emma identify Dr. Van Helsing in her paper?

———

REFLECTION: Evolving Ethical Norms

MEDICAL ETHICS AND research norms are constantly evolving. Some of the profession's most illustrious figures have engaged in conduct that in hindsight is difficult to defend. For example, Jonas Salk, the celebrated inventor of the polio vaccine, previously took part in conducting controversial research that sprayed "wild influenza" into the nasal passages of psychiatric patients. J. Marion Simms, the father of modern gynecology, earned his initial fame for performing experimental surger ies on unanesthetized African American slaves. Experiments that went largely unremarked upon at the time—such as the notorious Tuskegee syphilis experiment (1932–1972), in which poor black men were denied a treatment for their disease so that government researchers could watch its natural course— now appear deeply unethical. Only over the past few decades has medicine made a concerted effort to clear the historical record. For instance, diseases named for Nazi physicians Friedrich Wegener (1907–1990) and Hans Reiter (1881–1969) have recently been renamed. A statue of Simms was removed from Central Park in 2018.

Contemporary society places considerable emphasis on acknowledgement of past mistakes and often favors candor over retribution. One can see this phenomenon in the operation of "truth and reconciliation" in nations as varied as Argentina and South Africa. Yet the revelation of a highly regarded figure's shady past not only damages that individual's image, but it may also undermine the ability of that individual to champion worthwhile causes. For instance, revelations that German Nobel laureate Günter Grass served in the Waffen-SS during World War II led to what Grass's biographer called "the end of a moral institution" and the end of his authority to speak convincingly on behalf of human rights around the world.

The experiment in which Dr. Van Helsing participated as a college student clearly defies modern ethical standards. But such experiments were all too common prior to the revolution in patients' rights that occurred in the 1960s and 1970s. Even if his involvement was minor, an argument can be made that history should judge his participation. Emma may owe it to the children he sickened to reveal her discovery. Yet exposure would likely prevent Van Helsing from continuing his patient advocacy and human rights work. An argument can be made for forgoing justice for Van Helsing's past victims if doing so will help save present-day lives, but such a utilitarian approach may sit uneasily with many people.

PART TWO

Body Parts

The advent of specialized surgeries in the twentieth century, and especially organ transplantation, has raised a novel set of ethical concerns. Richard Lawler of Little Company of Mary Hospital in Illinois performed the first cadaveric kidney transplant in 1950, and Joseph Murray of Boston's Brigham Hospital performed the first successful living kidney transplant in 1954, but transplantation remained relatively rare and extremely risky for the next three decades. That changed in 1983, when the immunosuppressive agent cyclosporine came to market. Yet as organ transplantation became safer and more frequent, physicians had to grapple with the ethics of how to allocate scares organs. What factors, if any—medical, social, moral—should exclude a patient from eligibility for life-saving treatment?

Beyond the realm of transplantation, technological advances also made possible novel procedures in gender reassignment, reconstructive cosmetics, and body modification. Which operations should be permitted—and who should pay for these often-costly interventions—remains a source of considerable debate.

13

"Take My Foot, Please"

Margaret, a forty-year-old teacher, is a new patient of Dr. McCoy, a prominent orthopedic surgeon. At their initial appointment, when he asks how he can help her, Margaret replies, "I want you to amputate my left foot." Further discussion and examination reveals that Margaret's foot is physically healthy and not a source of pain or disability.

Margaret elaborates: "All my life, I've had this strange feeling that my left foot—right here, below the ankle—did not feel like it was part of my body. I have been to psychiatrists and neurologists, but nobody can explain it. To me, even though the foot functions just fine, it feels like having a foreign object attached to my leg. Then last year, I went online and discovered that there are other people out there like me who suffer from 'foreign limb syndrome'—who have limbs or appendages that feel like they do not belong. We are sort of like patients who want sex-change operations, only far fewer medical professionals take us seriously.

"Can you please amputate my foot safely? I will be glad to undergo a complete psychiatric evaluation first to show you I am not mentally ill. Honestly, if no surgeon will help me, I would do it myself with a saw—but I am afraid I might bleed to death."

Assuming a mental health examination reveals no psychiatric illness, should Dr. McCoy perform this amputation on Margaret?

REFLECTION: Elective Limb Amputation

Body identity integrity disorder (BIID) remains one of the most puzzling—and for many people, unsettling—diagnoses in modern medicine. Patients describe experiencing xenomelia, or the sense that a part of their body is foreign. For some, there is a connection to a related condition, apotemnophilia, in which the patient often finds the image of himself as an amputee sexually gratifying, but this link is far from universal. Usually, feelings that a limb is foreign begin at an early age. One theory posits that the phenomenon is entirely neurological and reflects an error in neural circuitry that prevents the brain from registering the particular body part as "self." Critics of this hypothesis invoke a psychiatric basis for the condition—possibly the result of early childhood trauma. Some psychiatrists have suggested a connection to body dysmorphic disorder, an anxiety disorder of distorted body image, but most BIID patients strongly reject this theory. Patients seeking elective amputations frequently draw direct parallels to individuals who seek gender-reassignment surgery in order to conform their bodies to their underlying gender identities. Whatever its cause, individuals with BIID suffer considerably.

Instances of patients seeking elective limb amputation date back at least as far as 1785. In 2012, Guardian columnist Mo Costandi reporting finding a case from a medical textbook by French physician Jean-Joseph Sue of a man "who fell in love with a one-legged woman, and wanted to become an amputee himself so that he could win her heart." According to the case history, the man forced a surgeon to perform the operation at gunpoint. The first modern instance was reported by noted sexologist John Money in 1977. Several hundred other cases have since been documented. How to handle these patients remains the subject of considerable controversy.

Doctors are generally trained to follow the principle of non-malfeasance or "do no harm"; the prospect of amputating a healthy limb may strike them as anathema. Yet BIID patients can and often do risk their own lives—and occasionally those of others—to achieve their ends when their pleas are rejected by physicians. For instance, sufferers have reportedly placed affected limbs on railroad tracks to achieve amputation. In the late 1990s, a Scottish surgeon named Robert Smith performed elective limb amputation on two patients before his country's National Health Service prohibited the procedure. Chloe Jennings-White, an American BIID patient who does not wish to feel her legs, had reportedly found a surgeon willing to sever her femoral and sciatic nerves, but could not yet afford the $25,000+ price tag.

In deciding whether to let Dr. McCoy honor Margaret's request, one might ask who will support Margaret in her new condition. Will she be eligible for government disability payments? And even if she is working now, what about in the future? One might also consider the possibility that neurologists or psychologists will develop a "cure" for BIID that allows patients to reintegrate their "foreign" limbs into their senses of self. Such a cure would arrive too late for those who have already sacrificed arms or legs, so in offering Dr. McCoy guidance, one must balance that future possibility against the current suffering of patients like Margaret.

14

Should She Stop Growing?

CLIFFORD AND CARLA have a six-year-old daughter, Charity, who suffers from profound intellectual disabilities. She cannot speak, walk, or hold her head upright and has the cognitive skills of a four-month-old baby. Clifford and Carla are loving parents—they have four other children—and they are determined to care for their disabled daughter at home and to integrate her into their family. Yet they are concerned that as she grows, she will prove too difficult to manage. Specifically, they are worried that they will no longer be able to carry her around the house or transport her easily on family events, such as picnics and outings to the aquarium. They are also concerned that when she reaches puberty, she might become an easy target for sexual abuse.

To protect their daughter, Carla and Clifford seek hormonal therapy that will close the growth plates in her bones, ensuring that she will permanently have the body of a six-year-old child. They also wish to put her on a hormonal regimen that will prevent puberty.

Should the doctors permanently "freeze" Charity in her six-year-old body at her parents' request?

REFLECTION: Growth-Attenuation Therapy

THE THERAPY CARLA and Clifford seek for Charity is not very different from the intervention performed upon a child then known only as Ashley X at Seattle's Children's Hospital and Regional Medical Center starting in 2004. Ashley, also called the "Pillow Angel" by her family, suffered from a potentially debilitating condition, static encephalopathy, which in her case left her with limited motor skills and the cognitive abilities of an infant. At the age of six, the girl showed signs of precocious puberty—a common phenomenon in neurologically compromised children. Her parents, reportedly hoping to increase her comfort and make caring for her easier, sought a series of medical procedures, including a hysterectomy, to prevent menstruation, breast bud removal, a prophylactic appendectomy, and hormonal therapies to close her growth plates prematurely. They accepted the small degree of risk involved in the surgeries.

As a result of these interventions, physicians Daniel Gunther and Douglas Diekema achieved their goal of reducing the girl's height by an estimated 20 percent and her weight by an estimated 40 percent. However, these "growth-attenuation treatments" generated considerable conflict within the bioethics community and among the public more generally. The hospital itself had to apologize for breaking the law, because it failed to obtain a court order before performing the hysterectomy despite a state statute requiring a judicial ruling for involuntary sterilization.

Many disability rights advocates and feminists criticize the surgery, which has become known as "the Ashley Treatment," as an affront to the dignity and the potential of the incapacitated child. Detractors also argue that the alleged need for the procedures reflects a failure of the social service system to provide adequate care and support for children like Ashley. Arthur Caplan, a leading bioethicist who opposed the intervention, told CNN, "I think mutilating surgery involving removal of breast buds is indefensible under any circumstances. . . . Growth retardation is not a substitute for adequate home aides and home assistance." Essayist Nancy Gibbs in Time asked rhetorically, regarding the claim that Ashley's decreased size would enable her parents to transport her on family outings more easily: "How far would Drs. Gunther and Diekema take this argument? Would they agree to amputate a child's legs to keep her lighter and more portable?" Most unsettling was a critique penned by Anne McDonald, a wheelchair-bound Australian woman with static encephalopathy who had been mistakenly diagnosed as "severely retarded" at age three. If it could happen to her, why not to Ashley?

Yet Gunther and Diekema also had their defenders. These included Ashley's parents. Ashley's father, in an interview with the Guardian, noted that "no amount of resources can replace the direct benefits to Ashley that the treatment provides" in terms of decreased pain and increased levels of comfort. He expressed regret that the public had not focused upon the "unique" nature of Ashley's impairments or the "significant and direct benefits" that she had obtained from the treatment.

Whether one supports or opposes growth-attenuation therapy for children like Ashley and Charity, a consensus exists that such interventions should only occur in the most extreme cases. As of 2016, at least sixty-five other children have undergone growth-attenuation therapy.

15

"She Must Be Marriageable"

A COUPLE ORIGINALLY from Ethiopia takes their five-year-old daughter, Eden, to a pediatric clinic in the United States, requesting female genital cutting be performed on their child. The mother explains that they are returning to Ethiopia permanently the following month and that they want the surgery done hygienically in a medical setting, rather than by an elder in their village, where the practice is far less safe and where children often suffer complications. According to the parents, their daughter will not be "marriageable" in Ethiopia without the surgery.

Female genital cutting, also known as "female circumcision," is a procedure in which sections of the female genitals are removed as part of a cultural ritual common in parts of Africa, Asia, and the Middle East. The procedure is associated with decreased sexual function and pleasure. Also, when performed under substandard medical conditions, it can lead to infection and even death.

Should the doctors at this clinic perform a "circumcision" on this girl in the United States to prevent the risk of worse harms befalling her in Ethiopia?

REFLECTION: Female Genital Cutting

FEMALE GENITAL CUTTING (FGC) has never been part of the Western tradition, and various efforts have been made to stamp out the practice in Africa and Asia, dating back at least as far as missionary John Arthur and the Church of Scotland's war against the practice in Kenya in the early 1930s. The United States formally banned the practice in 1996. Twenty-seven states also have laws criminalizing FGC. Even so, in 2000, the African Women's Health Center at Harvard's Brigham and Women's Hospital estimated that about 228,000 American women have either undergone the procedure or at risk. While criminal charges have occurred in the US—most prominently, the prosecution of Khalid Adem for cutting his two-year-old daughter's genitals with scissors—they have been relatively infrequent. In 2017, Jumana Nagarwala of Michigan became one of the first physicians in the US charged with engaging in the practice, but those charges were later dismissed when a federal judge ruled the law unconstitutional in November 2018. Some families of African and Middle Eastern origin continue to take "circumcision vacations" back in their native countries, or, less frequently, bring elders and midwives to the United States to perform the surgery in secret.

Critics refer to the procedure as "female genital mutilation" and cite the sexual and medical consequences, although significant disagreement exists over the safety of the operation. They also argue that FGC denies autonomy to young children, who cannot meaningfully consent to it. Yet not all Westerners condemn female circumcision. Some anthropologists view the effort to eradicate the procedure as a form of cultural imperialism. It is also worth noting that there exists a movement for the elimination of male circumcision on similar grounds, relating to the denial of autonomy and loss of sexual satisfaction, although these "intactivist" efforts are far less widespread. In 2012, a regional court in Cologne, Germany, classified male circumcision as child abuse, but this verdict has since been overruled by the Bundestag.

Complicating Eden's case is the parents' plan to relocate with her. If one takes at face value that the girl will not be marriageable in Ethiopia without having the procedure performed, which is likely true, her personal welfare might actually be served by FGC. However, engaging in the practice furthers the tradition and will continue to place other families in a similarly taxing position. One might reframe the scenario this way: There are some things that physicians (or people more generally) ought never to do. There are other things that physicians (or people) may do only under distinctive and extenuating circumstances. Eden's case asks one to decide which of these principles applies to female genital cutting.

16

"Give Her My Liver"

ELLEN IS THE single mother of a four-year-old girl, Alice. After Alice's health deteriorates progressively over several months, the child is diagnosed with a rare degenerative disorder that requires a liver transplant. Without a transplant in six months to one year, Alice will die. Unfortunately, the waiting list for cadaveric livers (i.e., livers from deceased donors) is extremely long; the majority of patients die before a liver becomes available. Fortunately, since 1989, some parents willing to serve as "living donors" have been able to give partial transplants to their children. The procedure poses a substantial danger to donors, however: between 1 in 200 and 1 in 600 die. Doctors are reluctant to perform such a risky operation on a healthy person, but will do so in cases where the donor is a close family member with a deep commitment to the child. Ellen researches this procedure and decided that she wants to donate part of her liver to Alice.

During the preliminary workup, doctors discover that Ellen was born with an unusual configuration of the blood vessels in her abdomen. They estimate that her chance of death, if they go through with the transplantation process, is closer to 1 in 4. This does not deter Ellen, but her surgeons are reluctant to go forward.

Should the doctors permit Ellen to take such a serious risk to increase the odds of saving her daughter's life?

———∿∿———

REFLECTION: Live Organ Donation

LIVING DONOR LIVER transplantation (LDLT) has been controversial since Christoph Broelsch performed the first such operation at the University of Chicago Medical Center in 1989. A handful of high-profile deaths, most notably that of donor Mike Hurewitz at New York's Mount Sinai Medical Center in 2002, have heavily influenced the availability of the procedure. Yet such transplants can and do save lives. With a chronic shortage of available organs, donors are often willing to take substantial risks to help their loved ones.

A serious concern in the consent process for such donors is that they may underestimate the dangers. Following the unexpected death of Paul Hawks in 2010, another supposedly healthy donor, surgeon James Markmann, chief of transplantation at Massachusetts General Hospital, told the Boston Globe, "You can quote 1 in 1,000 people will die and they think it's not going to happen to me because it's such a small number." While such underestimates can occur with any medical intervention, the difference here is that the donor is healthy and receives no medical benefit from the surgery; any advantage she garners is entirely psychological or social. Since most LDLTs occur between close relatives, there is also the risk of duress. Ascertaining whether a brother really wants to give a liver to his sister or feels obliged to do so (by family pressure, guilt, etc.) is a determination that doctors are particularly ill-equipped to handle.

When the risks jump from 1 in 100 to 1 in 4, doctors are faced with an additional challenge: How much risk should they allow any individual person to accept? If one is willing to permit Ellen to assume a 25 percent chance of death to save her daughter, what about a 50 percent chance or a 75 percent chance? What if the odds were 1 in 200 that she might survive the surgery? One can easily imagine a parent willing to risk her life at significant odds, or even sacrifice her life entirely, to save a beloved child. Those desires may be sincere and heartfelt. To what extent a person should be allowed to act on these feelings is one of the challenges of modern transplant ethics.

Oddly enough, the degree of risk that any potential donor may accept is often influenced by the nature of the system for evaluating transplant programs. Teams and hospitals are rated, in part, on the mortality of both donors and recipients—and those institutions which fare poorly can ultimately be shut down. Any transplant team willing to permit a patient with a 25 percent chance of dying to donate a liver to her child would certainly want to consider the impact on its program's overall success rate. In addition to the risk of government sanction, the optics of a mother perishing under such circumstances would look awful for the hospital and its surgeons; on the other hand, a successful transplant would likely generate substantial positive publicity.

17

"Am I My Brother's Donor?"

MORTY DEVELOPS AN acute form of leukemia, a blood cancer, and likely requires a hematopoietic stem cell transplant (sometimes referred to as a bone marrow transplant) to survive. Unfortunately, he has a rare tissue type, for which there are no current matches in any bone marrow registry database. His only hope, his doctors tell him, is a stem cell donation from a relative. Such a donation no longer even involves bone marrow—it requires taking medication for a few days and then having one's blood filtered through a machine for six hours. The procedure is mildly inconvenient, but generally without significant pain or long-term risks. It can be done as an outpatient, and the donor may resume normal activities within hours.

Morty has only one living relative—his brother, Lou. Lou suffers from significant intellectual disabilities and lives in a nursing facility. He cannot possibly understand the reasons for donating stem cells to Morty or the minor risks involved. What he does say, when asked, is "No doctors!" over and over again. Morty visits Lou a few times each year, usually bringing along a stuffed animal, and Lou appears to take pleasure in these visits, although the brothers have never had a close relationship.

Is it ethical for doctors to give Lou a mild sedative and filter his blood in order to try to save Morty's life?

REFLECTION: The Unwilling Donor

US LAW RECOGNIZES very few circumstances in which people owe duties to provide assistance to others without voluntary agreements to do so. Certain relationships do impose obligations, such as financial support for spouses and children. Most states require individuals who begin to help a stranger during an emergency to continue rendering such assistance, to the best of their abilities, until help arrives—as "partial rescues" run the risk of scaring off other would-be rescuers. Otherwise, only a handful of states compel innocent bystanders to offer emergency assistance. Courts have generally proven unwilling to force individuals to provide sick relatives with medical aid, such as organs or tissues, even when these individuals are uniquely situated to help. In one notorious case, David Shimp refused to give bone marrow to his cousin Robert McFall, who suffered from aplastic anemia, despite an estimated 50–60 percent chance of saving McFall's life. Although Judge John Flaherty Jr. derided Shimp's conduct as "morally indefensible," he did not compel the donation—and McFall died of his disease. Similarly, in another high-profile case, Tamas Bosze, the father of a boy with leukemia, was unable to convince a judge to order bone marrow testing on his other two children, the boy's half siblings, over the vehement objections of his estranged ex-wife.

More challenging are cases where the potential donor is cognitively impaired to the point where he cannot understand what is being asked of him. In the scenario of Morty and Lou, Lou may cry out against doctors, but conjecturing on whether he would consent to a brief medical procedure in order to continue to enjoy the occasional company of his brother is a purely speculative endeavor. No consensus exists on how to handle such situations. Doctors can sometimes turn to the patient's closest relative for guidance, but in Lou's case, that relative has an obvious conflict of interest.

One Kentucky court in 1969 went so far as to order Jerry Strunk, a cognitively impaired twenty-seven-year-old, to donate a kidney to his brother. More often, a complex cost-benefit analysis comes into play—one that weighs the hardship to the potential donor, the stakes for the potential recipient, and the emotional benefit that the recipient's survival affords the donor. In this case, Morty's life hangs in the balance while the costs to Lou are low, so the doctors might be able to justify obtaining a court order for the procedure. Yet one ought not lose sight of Lou's vulnerability as a person unable to fend for himself. As the potential medical risks of an intervention rise, the arguments for invading a person's bodily integrity prove increasingly more challenging to justify.

18

Organs for Celebrities

ROY WAS A star Major League Baseball player. After his retirement, he develops a severe alcohol problem that leads to acute liver failure. Without a liver transplant, he will die. He is currently a patient at Legends Hospital.

It is a long-standing policy at Legends, and at most (but not all) hospitals across the country, that patients must demonstrate six months of sobriety before receiving a liver transplant. This policy—which is not a law, merely a widely followed guideline—prevents active alcoholics from receiving livers, which they are likely to damage with additional drinking. Roy, unfortunately, arrived at the hospital drunk and in partial liver failure three days earlier; he cannot wait six months.

Dr. Diver, the senior transplant surgeon, tells her team to list Roy as a candidate for a liver transplant. "He's an alcoholic, and he'll likely lose the liver," says Dr. Diver. "But there's always some possibility that he'll turn himself around. And if he does, do you realize what a successful transplant for a famous patient like Roy will do for organ donation? Consider how many more people will agree to be organ donors! In the long run, we'll save thousands of lives!"

Is it ethical to make Roy a liver candidate for the reasons advanced by Dr. Diver?

<hr />

REFLECTION: Favoritism

A LONG-STANDING PERCEPTION exists—whether accurate or not—that celebrities receive favoritism in the allocation of scarce organs. During his second term in office, Governor Robert Casey of Pennsylvania received a heart-and-liver transplant after waiting for a donor less than twenty four hours in 1993. Television actor Jim Nabors and singer David Crosby obtained livers in under a month, while the median waiting time is 208 days. Yet few organ recipients have generated as much controversy as baseball slugger Mickey Mantle, who received a liver one day after announcing he needed a transplant in 1995, and died two months later of liver cancer. Whether or not Mantle benefited from favoritism—and there is no compelling evidence at this point that he did—the possibility that he had "jumped the line" generated much public criticism, as well as soul-searching among transplant providers and ethicists. Mantle's own transplant team was concerned that the appearance of favoritism would do damage to the organ allocation system.

Concern for the perception of favoritism is an ongoing issue in the allocation of organs that extends beyond celebrities. For example, an organization called Renewal, founded in 2006, has worked to further altruistic kidney donation within the Jewish community. The donors are generally ultra-Orthodox Jews seeking to do a good deed, or mitzvah. Only half of the recipients are religious, yet all but one have been Jewish—reflecting an unspoken principle underlying Renewal's recruitment system. In the Forward, writer Paul Berger estimated that while Hasidic and Haredi Jews account for 0.2 percent of the US population, they made up 17 percent of all altruistic kidney donations in 2014.

Advocates for allowing such religiously targeted donations note that they not only save lives in one particular group, but they also free up organs that can be used by others on the waiting list. If Renewal arranges for a Jewish patient to receive a kidney, that is one fewer person ahead of a non-Jew waiting for a kidney. Alternatively, without Renewal, these donors would likely not donate any organs at all. Critics object that should people come to perceive the organ donation system as favoring certain ethnic groups, people of other backgrounds may prove reluctant to donate organs in the future—and the overall pool of donor kidneys might actually decline.

In the case of baseball star Roy, Dr. Diver wants to alter the criteria for eligibility. The United Network for Organ Sharing (UNOS) uses criteria known as the Model for End-Stage Liver Disease (MELD) score in determining who receives cadaveric livers—generally allocating them to the sickest patients. Yet transplant teams also evaluate patients for eligibility based upon social and psychological criteria. The goal of these screenings is to weed out potential recipients who will be unable to take care of transplanted organs—either because they lack social support or are unlikely to comply with the complex regimen of follow-up care that successful transplantation requires.

Although active alcohol use has historically been an exclusionary criterion, because it may predict long-term transplant failure, a few medical centers have recently pioneered transplants in patients with acute-onset alcoholic hepatitis. Giving transplants to otherwise-qualified alcoholics who pledge to stop drinking is highly controversial; long-term data does not yet exist on the outcomes of these cases. Advocates argue that alcoholism must be treated as a disease like any other—and such patients should be afforded the benefit of the doubt. Critics note that, in the context of a widespread organ shortage, each organ given to an alcohol abuser means a nonabuser waiting for an organ will die, while there is a strong chance the organ recipient will prove noncompliant and die too.

A utilitarian argument—favoring the greatest good for the greatest number of people—does not necessary favor Dr. Diver's approach. It is possible that a successful transplant for a celebrity athlete like Roy would generate more donor organs, but another, more troublesome possibility also exists: the public would perceive favoritism in an allocation process that advantages the wealthy and famous, which would lead to fewer donations.

19

Ads for Organs

TEX IS A wealthy oil tycoon in need of a liver transplant. Since the waiting list for livers is long, he decides to take matters into his own hands. He places billboards all over his state that read TEX NEEDS A LIVER. PLEASE HELP! HE ADVERTISES ON BOTH RADIO AND TELEVISION, ASKING ANYONE WITH A LOVED ONE WHO IS IN A FATAL ACCIDENT TO EARMARK THE VICTIM'S LIVER TO GO SPECIFICALLY TO TEX. IN THE ADS, TEX TOUTS HIM-SELF AS A MODEL CITIZEN, A VETERAN, A CHURCHGOER, AND A PATRON OF THE ARTS.

Soon after the billboards go up, the wife of an unconscious patient on life support announces that she will donate her husband's organs only if the liver goes to Tex. In Tex's state, hospitals generally will not authorize transplants unless the patient has given written instructions in advance or the patient's nearest relative consents.

Should Tex be able to "jump the line" and solicit a heart in this way?

———∾∾———

REFLECTION: The Free Market of Medicine

ADVERTISING IS BOTH ubiquitous and highly efficacious. In 2014, the nonprofit organization Re-Born to be Alive hired Belgian advertising firm Duval-Guillaume to promote organ donation. The result was a series of ads that depicted individuals engaged in foolish, life-threatening behavior (e.g., using a blowtorch alongside an oxygen tank) with the tagline "8 of his organs can be donated. Luckily for us his brain is not one of them." The campaign was noncontroversial and highly successful. More contentious are efforts by private individuals, like Tex, to advertise for organs on their own.

In the United States, the allocation of most organs is managed by the United Network for Organ Sharing, a nonprofit organization that follows rules enacted by the US Department of Health and Human Services. The so-called Final Rule of March 2000, which governs the allocation of organs, allows donors to earmark their body parts in advance of their deaths. And under limited circumstances, this approach makes sense: If the close relative of a patient on the waiting list dies suddenly, a strong moral case can be made for allowing the family to transfer the organ to their own kin—as doing so likely would fulfill the wishes of the deceased, may tip those on the fence into donation, and does not in any substantial way undermine the fairness of the existing system. Presumably, the rich and powerful are no more likely to benefit from such intrafamilial allocations than the indigent.

In the years following the enactment of the Final Rule, well-off individuals like Tex have taken to advertising for organs. In 2004, cancer patient Todd Krampitz of Houston advertised for a new liver on billboards, ultimately receiving a liver from an anonymous family that earmarked the organ specifically for him. (Krampitz, thirty-two years old, died of his disease eight months afterward.) A year later, thirty-one-year-old Red Cross publicist Shari Kurzrok, diagnosed with acute liver failure, advertised for a donor in the New York Times. (She ultimately received a liver from the waiting list, married, became a mother, and has enjoyed a successful career in advertising.) Ethicists and transplant physicians remain deeply divided on the ethics of these maneuvers.

Critics like New York University's Arthur Caplan argue that allowing patients like Krampitz and Kurzrok to jump the line undermines the fairness of the system. Under federal law, organs are supposed to be allocated to those patients most in need, regardless of wealth or influence—and allowing the rich and powerful to run ad campaigns circumvents that principle. The risk also exists that others will perceive the system as unjust and will refuse to donate. As a result, UNOS and the American Society of Transplant Surgeons have both issued statements opposed to such advertising campaigns, including open solicitation on the internet and social media.

Yet even without advertising, donors from the community

often step forward to give organs to celebrities. Supporters of advertising are aware of the potential image problems created by such donations, but believe that the practice will increase the overall availability of organs. For example, there is no reason to believe that the family who donated to Todd Krampitz would have given an organ otherwise; any patients who secure outside organs through advertising, the thinking goes, also free up organs for others on the waiting list.

In 2005, Alex Crionas learned the hard way precisely how divided the medical community remains on the subject of advertising for organs. He had lined up a kidney donor, Patrick Garrity, only to be refused a transplant by his local hospital's transplant-coordinating nonprofit because he had advertised for a donor online. (Ironically, he had not met Garrity through his online ads.) Fortunately for Crionas, he was able to transfer his care to another hospital, which performed the transplant successfully with no ethical objections.

20

Transplantation on Death Row

JANET IS AN inmate on death row. She was accused of killing her stepmother with an ax—a charge she adamantly denies—and was convicted three months ago. Her case is now on appeal. Typically in the state where she was tried, ten to fifteen years elapse between conviction and execution, and 50 percent of defendants initially sentenced to death end up having their sentences either overturned or commuted.

While in prison, Janet develops partial heart failure due to a viral infection. She will require a heart transplant to survive. On a positive note, because she is a prisoner, she would likely receive excellent and consistent medical care to ensure the survival of a transplanted heart. At the same time, since hearts are scarce, if Janet were to receive a heart, someone else on the waiting list would likely die while waiting.

Should Janet be eligible for a heart transplant?

REFLECTION: **Prisoners' Rights**

THE US SUPREME Court ruled in Estelle v. Gamble (1976) that prisoners cannot be discriminated against in the delivery of medical care. Denying healthcare to inmates, who are at the mercy of the state, amounts to "cruel and unusual punishment." As a result, convicts facing stiff terms of incarceration have received costly government-financed organ transplants—including a California robber who garnered a $1 million heart transplant during the fourth year of a fourteen-year sentence and a Minnesota murderer who benefited from a $900,000 bone marrow transplant. Yet organs are scarce resources—and in the case of an inmate facing execution, some might view transplantation as effectively squandering a lifesaving organ.

The media often focuses on death row inmates who wish to donate organs prior to, or at the time of, their executions. In 2011, Governor Haley Barbour of Mississippi freed Jamie and Gladys Grant, two sisters facing life in prison for robbery, so that one could donate a lifesaving kidney to the other—a decision criticized by some ethicists as conditioning release on organ donation. Christian Longo, an Oregon inmate facing lethal injection for killing his wife and three young children, founded an organization called Gifts of Anatomical Value From Everyone, which seeks to allow death row inmates to donate their organs. Indiana killer Gregory Scott Johnson unsuccessfully sought a stay of execution in 2005 in order to donate a liver to his ill sister. Critics of allowing death row inmates to donate organs fear that prisoners will act in the hope of obtaining clemency or that the state will coerce such donations, as is rumored to occur in several foreign nations.

If condemned prisoners rarely offer to donate organs, still rarer is the death row inmate who seeks listing to receive an organ. The most prominent case is probably that of Horacio

Alberto Reyes-Camarena, a convicted killer from Oregon who sought a kidney transplant in 2003.

A consensus exists among all stakeholders in the organ allocation system that perceived social worth will generally not be considered in the distribution of organs. Factors like one's economic status, occupation, and contribution to society should play no role in determining who receives a lifesaving heart or liver. Notably, this was not always the case with critical interventions. In 1962, Seattle's King County Medical Society established a so-called "God committee" that did use social worth as a determinant in allocating scarce dialysis treatments. A profile of the committee's deliberations in Life led to public outrage—and ultimately, to federal funding for all dialysis care.

In contrast, while social worth is not considered an acceptable factor in allocating organs, some degree of controversy remains regarding whether "moral responsibility" for one's illness should play any role in the recipient selection process. This debate has largely focused on alcoholics and drug users seeking liver transplants—with the current approach excluding moral responsibility as a factor in allocation. An alcoholic may be denied a liver because of his current drinking habits or his likelihood of relapse, but not because he caused his liver to fail. Suicidal patients who remain at high risk of repeat attempts raise similar concerns.

In the case of death row inmates, one might argue that denying prisoners like Janet organs has nothing to do with their crimes, only with impending punishments that will reduce the life expectancy of the organs. Yet in many jurisdictions, the average death row inmate spends more time awaiting execution than the average transplanted organ survives—even with excellent medical care. Reyes-Camarena is himself an example of this irony. The life expectancy of a cadaveric kidney, for instance, is roughly thirteen years. Sentenced to death in 1997 and denied an organ transplant in 2003, Reyes-Camarena remains on Oregon's death row more than fifteen years later.

21

A Chimp Heart

BABY SHIRLEY IS a five-month-old girl with a severe congenital heart defect. Without a transplant in weeks, she is likely to die. The odds of a heart becoming available during that period are low—maybe 20 percent at best.

Her cardiologist, Dr. Welby, approaches Baby Shirley's parents, George and Gertrude, with a novel idea. "We could try implanting a baby chimpanzee heart," he says. "It's never been done before, but I think it's worth a shot—better than waiting for a twenty percent chance of an organ becoming available while watching your daughter die. It would also be a great step forward for science if we succeeded." A live chimpanzee would have to be euthanized for this transplant to occur.

Is transplanting a chimpanzee heart into Baby Shirley ethical under these circumstances?

REFLECTION: Xenotransplantation

THE HISTORY OF xenotransplantation—the transplanting of organs across species—is largely a history of disappointed hopes. In 1963–1964, at a time before dialysis or human organs were widely available, surgeon Keith Reemtsma transplanted chimpanzee kidneys into thirteen human patients; the longest-surviving recipient lived nine months. In 1964, three years before Christiaan Barnard performed the first human-to-human heart transplant, James Hardy transplanted a chimpanzee heart into a dying patient, Boyd Rush; Rush died within two hours. Thomas Starzl attempted chimpanzee-to-human liver transplants on children in 1966, 1969, and 1974. None succeeded. (On Starzl's fourth try at xenotransplantation, in 1992, the human recipient of a baboon liver survived seventy days.) Likely the best-known and most controversial case of xenotransplantation occurred in 1984, at California's Loma Linda University Medical Center, when Leonard L. Bailey transplanted a baboon heart into an infant suffering from hypoplastic left heart syndrome. "Baby Fae" rejected the organ twenty-one days later. Her case generated considerable negative publicity for animal-to-human transplants.

Bailey had made no attempt to find a human heart for transplant prior to the surgery, a decision later strongly criticized by many ethicists. While some supporters compared the case to that of Barney Clark, the dentist who received a "permanent" artificial heart in 1982, many bioethicists reject the comparison. Clark's doctors had sought—and found—no alternatives for their critically ill patient. He was also an adult, fully capable of consenting to the experimental treatment, while Baby Fae's team had relied upon the permission of the child's parents. A leading health scholar, George Annas, asked in the Christian

Science Monitor in 1984: "Are we getting back to the old days when doctors just experimented [on people]?" In Time, columnist Charles Krauthammer derided the surgery as "an adventure in medical ethics." Bailey did not help his own case any when he revealed publicly that he did not believe in evolution—a disclosure that damaged his credibility among a significant segment of the public.

Some opponents argue that xenotransplantation, since it violates the boundaries between species and threatens human uniqueness, could never be ethical—even if it proved highly efficacious. And animal rights advocates question whether it should be permissible to kill a higher-order ape, such as a chimpanzee, to save a human life. Yet most bioethicists who object to xenotransplantation raise doubts about the process with regard to its experimental nature. In Baby Shirley's case, one must ask how one weighs the estimated 20 percent chance of the child receiving a human heart in time against the unknown odds of her surviving with a chimp organ. Is this a decision for her parents? For experts in transplantation? For society as a whole? From Dr. Welby's description, the girl's parents may have a difficult time discerning whether this transplant is primarily a therapeutic intervention or an experiment. At a minimum, before being allowed to consent to such a high-risk procedure, they should be informed of the grim historical context: if past experience is any indication, Dr. Welby's proposed surgery appears unlikely to work.

22

A Head Case

DON, A FORTY-YEAR-OLD neurosurgeon, has been diagnosed with terminal pancreatic cancer and has only several months left to live. His colleague, Dr. Pangloss, suggests to him that his disease might afford them an opportunity to try the experiment they have both longed to perform—a human head transplant. Their goal is to attach Don's head—and brain—to a human body healthy from the neck down.

Dr. Pangloss believes he can persuade the family of a skull trauma patient to donate such a body. He also believes that—with the help of surgeons from many fields—he can connect Don's spine and blood vessels to the donor's cadaver. Most likely, Don will end up paralyzed below the neck, but Dr. Pangloss holds out hope that some of the nerve fibers might connect and regenerate. "The odds are against us," says Dr. Pangloss. "But without daring, heroic measures, you'll be dead anyway." Except for his pancreatic tumor, Don is in excellent health and a great candidate for major surgery. Don and his family very much want to try the radical surgery. Private charities have agreed to cover the costs.

Should the hospital's ethics committee approve this first-ever attempt at a head transplant?

———∽∽———

REFLECTION: Experimental Transplants

BRAIN TRANSPLANTATION—OR WHOLE-BODY transplantation—
has long been a staple of science fiction. Iconic depictions
include the work of Martian surgeon Ras Thavas in Edgar Rice
Burroughs's The Master Mind of Mars (1927) and the experience
of patient Johann Sebastian Bach Smith in Robert Heinlein's I
Will Fear No Evil (1970). Barriers to such a procedure succeed-
ing in real life are substantial. Soviet experiments conducted
on puppies by Vladimir Demikhov during the 1950s proved
largely unsuccessful. In 1970, American neurosurgeon Robert
White (1926–2010) managed to transplant the head of one rhe-
sus monkey onto the decapitated body of another, although the
second animal's immune system ultimately rejected the new
head after nine days. In the interim, however, the transplanted
head was able to see, hear, smell, taste—and even tried to bite
a staff member. (White had already gained prominence in the
1960s for creating a "dog with two brains" by attaching an isolated canine brain to the blood vessels of another dog.) In 2018,
Italian physician Sergio Canavero and his Chinese colleague,
Xiaoping Ren of China, predicted that human head transplantation is "imminent," although these claims were met with
widespread skepticism in the mainstream medical community.
They say their goal is to give additional life to a terminally ill
patient such as Don.

Ethicists have been largely unsympathetic to these efforts.
Arthur Caplan, the dean of American bioethicists, wrote in

Forbes that "one would have to be out of one's mind" to attempt a brain transplant with existing technologies. Caplan noted that such an operation would require immunosuppressive drugs that have serious side effects and risks; life on such a medication regimen might prove miserable for the recipient. Rejection of transplanted organs would pose a particular challenge in this case—likely leading to a slow and potentially painful demise. The prospect for significant psychological distress should also be considered. Clint Hallam, recipient of the world's first hand transplant, eventually chose to have the limb amputated because he felt "mentally detached" from it. What if a head transplant recipient became similarly detached from his new body? Finally, the likelihood of reattaching spinal nerves without further technical advances seems highly unlikely. At best, Don would find himself a quadriplegic.

Balanced against these concerns stands the stark reality that, without the transplant, Don will soon die. The principle of autonomy argues for letting him make his own decisions. He is a neurosurgeon, after all—so he is likely to understand the dangers. Of course, the consequences of the surgery could prove horrific. Don might awaken to discover himself conscious but "locked" inside his own brain, without any sensory perception or ability to communicate. Even if a patient could truly anticipate and appreciate the torment that such a fate entails without actually having experienced it—which is questionable—one might ask whether there are some forms of suffering so horrific that no person should be permitted to risk them.

23

Reducing Sexual Urges

WARREN IS A fifty-two-year-old writer who has been troubled by sexual fantasies about underage boys and girls since his adolescence. Multiple trials of psychotherapy have done nothing to reduce his urges. A psychiatrist recommended chemical castration through hormonal injections, but Warren has learned that these treatments can increase his risk of having a stroke. Instead, he asks a surgeon in his community, Dr. Hunnicutt, to castrate him "the old-fashioned way." Warren is on Medicaid and has no money of his own.

Should Dr. Hunnicutt agree to remove Warren's testicles surgically?

REFLECTION: Voluntary Castration

CASTRATION—BOTH CHEMICAL AND surgical—has recently gained renewed attention from physicians and policy makers as a way to prevent recidivism, which is a problem among sex offenders. In the 1960s, sexologist John Money at Johns Hopkins University pioneered the use of a contraceptive hormone, medroxyprogesterone, to reduce libidinous urges among pedophiles. California imposed such treatment upon a small segment of repeat sex offenders in 1996. In 1997, then-governor George W. Bush signed legislation that made Texas the first state to allow prison inmates to choose surgical castration voluntarily. Over the past two decades, a number of states have enacted laws either allowing or requiring some form of castration for certain offenders. Often, these statutes operate in conjunction with "civil commitment" laws, which enable states to keep convicted sex offenders locked up in hospitals after their sentences have expired on the grounds of ongoing dangerousness. Some offenders elect for castration as a means of reducing unhealthy desires or demonstrating their commitment to avoiding future offenses. Critics condemn these policies as inherently coercive. They also note the significant medical risks and side effects involved in chemical castration and the irreversibility of the surgical procedure.

A meaningful assessment of the ethics of castration—whether forced or voluntary, surgical or chemical—might take into account its efficacy. Unfortunately, the data remain mixed. One widely cited German study, conducted by Reinhard Wille and Klaus Beier, reported only a 3 percent recidivism rate among castrated sex offenders, compared to a 46 percent rate among those not castrated. However, an analysis by Mary Barker and Rod Morgan in Great Britain questioned the effectiveness of such treatments, noting methodological problems in many studies. For instance, some researchers have included those convicted for consensual homosexual relationships among "sex offenders"—clearly creating a skewed and inappropriate sample. A comprehensive review of existing research, conducted by Linda Weinberger and colleagues, concluded that castration "alone, without attendant psychological change, may be insufficient to mitigate sexual recidivism in a person who is in the community and subject to temptations." Conflicting data might also reflect variability among the motives of so-called sex offenders. While some might commit their crimes as a result of pedophilic urges, others may be driven by anger or have acted under the influence of illicit drugs. These latter individuals appear less likely to be tempered by castration. In Warren's case, as his goal is to reduce sexual urges, castration may help, but it is also a significant and irreversible mutilation of his body.

Since Warren is on Medicaid, one must also decide whether the taxpayers should pick up the tab for his surgery. Warren might make his case on medical grounds—namely, that his urges are causing him significant psychological distress, and that no cheaper safe alternative treatment appears to be available. Or he could frame his argument in the name of the public welfare. Even if the odds of Warren acting on his fantasies are low—as he has not yet acted upon them in five decades—if he did, the consequences would be devastating. Preventing an episode of child abuse seems worth $18,000. The amount is also likely far less than the economic cost of trying and imprisoning an offender or providing social services for a victim. Opponents of such coverage might counter than this intervention is no different than other high-cost experimental medical interventions that are generally not covered by public insurance programs.

24

"Give Me a Horn"

MADDIE IS A prominent member of the body-modification community in her city. She has piercings in her ears, nose, eyebrows, and septum, and in numerous other places. She also has well over one hundred distinct tattoos. What she really wants, however, is a large fiberglass horn implanted in her skull so she can "look like a dinosaur."

She makes an appointment with Dr. Daneeka, a prominent plastic surgeon. She wants Dr. Daneeka to screw the horn into her skull surgically—a procedure for which she will pay cash. This is not a risk-free procedure. It requires general anesthesia, which carries some danger, and could result in blood loss or infection. And this particular operation has also never been done before, so there may be unanticipated consequences. Dr. Daneeka tentatively agrees to perform the surgery, pending approval from the ethics committee at his hospital.

Should the hospital ethics committee approve this novel procedure?

REFLECTION: Body Modifications

PHYSICIANS HAVE ALWAYS had a complex relationship with body modification. As advocates for the public health, doctors have championed restrictions on procedures considered dangerous. For example, the risk of hepatitis led medical groups to petition for bans on tattooing in the 1960s, such as those that were enacted in Massachusetts (1962–2000) and New York City (1961–1997). Yet as members of a guild, concerned for their "turf," physicians have also lobbied heavily to keep all body modification under the exclusive purview of the medical profession. In 1976, the Arkansas State Medical Board fought a legal battle with Edna Hicks, a cosmetologist who performed ear piercing in her shop. The medical board argued that the piercings were a form of surgery and constituted the practice of medicine, so they should only be available from a licensed physician—but the courts disagreed. Since that landmark case, a peculiar division of services appears to have arisen between individuals who perform so-called "cosmetic procedures," which are generally done by licensed medical professionals; and those who offer "body modification" services, which often occur in tattoo parlors. Yet the bounds between these two divergent worlds remain porous and subjective.

It is also worth noting that the line between a cosmetic procedure and a medically necessary one is highly problematic. For instance, should breast reconstruction after mastectomy be viewed as essential healthcare or an elective luxury? Congress waded into this debate in 1998, passing the Women's Health and Cancer Rights Act (WHCRA), which requires private insurers who cover mastectomies to cover reconstructive breast surgery too. In another well-known case, that of a teenager, Kevin Sampson, whose mother was a practicing Jehovah's Witness, the courts confronted the question of whether to order surgery for a facial growth that doctors described as unsightly but not life-threatening. Kevin's mother, Mildred, objected to the blood transfusion necessary for the surgery and argued that the procedure was purely cosmetic.

For ethicists and policy makers, the regulation of body-modification practices becomes most challenging with regard to interventions that pose some danger, especially when done in a private setting, yet which licensed health professionals are generally not interested in performing. One such phenomenon is tongue splitting or tongue forking. The procedure, which bifurcates the tongue through cutting or cauterization, sometimes allowing each fork to move separately, is desired by some for either aesthetic or sexual purposes, or both. It was popularized by a body-modification advocate nicknamed the Lizardman in the late 1990s. Although the Lizardman had his bifurcation performed by an oral surgeon, many others pursue the surgery at specialized parlors or perform it themselves, as did body-modification pioneer Dustin Allor in 1996, resulting in considerable publicity. Yet the procedure carries considerable risks—ranging from reduction of sensation to significant blood loss; in theory, severing an artery could lead to death. As a result, a number of states, starting with Illinois in 2003, have restricted the practice of tongue splitting to oral surgeons and related professionals. Yet oral surgeons are not racing to replace body-modification artists in this enterprise, so the result has been a decline in the availability of the procedure. In some places, the restrictions are, in practice, a de facto prohibition. Critics argue that the result has been an increase in risk to the community, as would-be tongue splitters are not deterred, but rather driven underground for surgery. "Corset piercing," along the spine, and eye tattooing raise similar issues.

One might take the absolutist position that hospitals should not permit any cosmetic procedures involving meaningful risk—including nose jobs, tummy tucks, and face-lifts, as well as breast reconstruction or enhancement. After all, doctors have a duty to do no harm. However, if one accepts the psychological benefits of cosmetic intervention as justifying these more common interventions, one is hard-pressed to argue against Dr. Daneeka's plans for Maddie. One woman's breast enhancement, after all, is another woman's giant fiberglass horn. Denying Maddie the appearance of her choosing seems both arbitrary and based upon culturally embedded norms that could easily change. Who can say that, in a generation, such horns will not be as common as pierced earlobes? More important, from the standpoint of health and safety, is that individuals seeking unconventional cosmetic procedures are not shut out by mainstream medicine, leading them to pursue high-risk surgeries conducted by amateurs in a black market.

25

Conjoined Twins At Odds

Lucy and Lily are eighteen-year-old conjoined twins. Unlike many of the conjoined twins depicted in the media, they dislike each other intensely and have deeply incompatible views about what it means to lead a meaningful life. To Lucy, life attached to Lily is intolerable, especially as it will likely prevent her from either pursuing a career as a surgeon or meeting a romantic partner and having a family. Lily, in contrast, is deeply religious and resigned to her fate.

The twins are conjoined in such a way that there is yet a hope for separating them. Surgeons estimate that the risk of death during the procedure for each twin is about 15 percent—but a 30 percent chance exists that at least one of them will die. For Lucy, this operation is worth the risk. She goes to court seeking a court order for the surgery. Lily objects.

For whom should the judge rule in this case?

REFLECTION: Quality of Life/Sanctity of Life

Conjoined twins are a relatively rare phenomenon. Estimates place the incidence of the condition as occurring once in 25,000 to 200,000 births. The public has long been fascinated by the lives of these attached siblings. In the nineteenth century, Thai brothers Chang and Eng Bunker, the so-called "Siamese twins," toured with P. T. Barnum's circus. African American sisters Millie and Christine McCoy gained international fame as the "the Two-Headed Nightingale" and "the Eighth Wonder of the World" in the same era. Many conjoined twins display high qualities of life, such as the widely profiled Abby and Brittany Hensel of Minnesota.

Byzantine doctors first separated a set of twins in the tenth century. Advances in surgery have allowed for more sophisticated procedures: in 1957, Bertram Katz divided Johnny and Jimmy Freeman, who had been born sharing a liver; Ben Carson made headlines in 1987 detaching the Binder twins, who had been joined at the back of the head. Yet not all conjoined twins can be separated—and often the surgery itself involves considerable risk. Sometimes, there is a 100 percent likelihood that one twin will die. This was the situation with Jodie and Mary, twins from Malta, whom an English court ordered separated in 2000 over their parents' objections. In that unique case, Mary was dependent upon the heart and lungs of Jodie—and was slowly draining Jodie of life. Without the operation, both girls were ultimately expected to perish.

Significant ethical questions arose when twenty-nine-year-old Iranian sisters Ladan and Laleh Bijani pursued separation surgery in Singapore that entailed a 50 percent chance of death or brain damage. They died during the 2003 operation. In that case, both sisters had sought surgery. More challenging would be a case where one of the siblings objects to the procedure. In many ways, this dilemma embodies the core conflict in contemporary bioethics: how to balance quality of life and sanctity of life. For Lucy, quality of life has dropped low enough that she will risk death to improve it. Lily, on the other hand, holds life sacred and is not willing to risk it to improve her lot. There are three possible resolutions for this scenario. One might decide that nobody should ever have to risk her life or undergo major elective surgery against her will, and side with Lily. Alternatively, one might rule for Lucy on the grounds that nobody should be forced to spend her life "chained" to another person. Finally, one might decide these matters on a case-by-case basis determined by survival odds. Many people would order the surgery if both twins had a 99 percent chance of surviving, but not if their odds of surviving were 1 percent. Where to draw the line, of course, proves difficult, especially if odds of one twin surviving differ from that of the other.

PART THREE

Making Babies

E thical decisions surrounding reproductive decision-making are among the most highly charged and controversial in the United States today. The series of Supreme Court cases surrounding the legalization of abortion, most notably Roe v. Wade (1973) and Planned Parenthood v. Casey (1992), have become polarizing events in the political process, and the "third rail" of federal judicial appointments. Yet the issues surrounding pregnancy and childbirth extend well beyond the likely irresolvable question of when life begins. Some of these questions derive from the increased social acceptance of so-called "nontraditional families"—itself a highly problematic term.

As individuals and couples of diverse gender identities and sexual orientations seek to bear and raise children, ethical and legal norms must evolve. But how? Advances in alternative reproductive technologies—from in vitro fertilization to pre-implantation genetic diagnosis—empower prospective parents and increase reproductive autonomy but also raise unsettling questions about their limits. Should anyone—of any age or of any moral character—be allowed to produce and raise children?

And should they be allowed to harness genetic innovations to decide which phenotypic traits will be reflected in their offspring? These questions are certainly not easy to answer, and new technologies are emerging at such rapid speeds that ethicists will likely always be developing and framing the issues.

26

A Child with a Purpose

HARRIET AND ARTHUR have a teenage son, Gary, who suffers from leukemia and requires a bone marrow donor. Unable to find a suitable match through existing donor databases, they decide to conceive a second child through in vitro fertilization, using new technologies to make sure this second child is a potential match. As Harriet and Arthur are already in their late forties and not prepared to raise a second child, they have arranged for the young married couple living next door to adopt the child. As part of the adoption agreement, it is understood that when the boy or girl is physically old enough to donate bone marrow, these neighbors will consent to the procedure on behalf of their adopted child.

Is it ethical for Harriet and Arthur to make this arrangement?

REFLECTION: Savior Siblings

THE DEVELOPMENT OF two distinct technologies, preimplantation genetic diagnosis (PGD) and human leukocyte antigen (HLA) testing, allows for the creation of "savior siblings," who can donate lifesaving tissue to brothers and sisters with otherwise fatal diseases. PGD enables parents to screen embryos in advance of implantation—choosing to implant only those that have the potential to save of the life of their existing child. HLA testing allows them to know which embryos to choose. In 2001, a team of researchers in Chicago, led by Yury Verlinsky, first reported using PGD to save the life of a patient with Fanconi's anemia. Pulitzer Prize–winning journalist Beth Whitehouse's The Match (2011), based on a series of Newsday articles, recounts one family's efforts to have a second child to save a daughter afflicted with Diamond Blackfan anemia. The savior-sibling concept also forms the basis for Jodi Picoult's best-selling novel My Sister's Keeper (2004). Great Britain's Human Fertilisation and Embryology Authority has authorized the practice, which is also widely available in the United States, although no reliable statistics are available on its frequency.

The creation of savior siblings is not without its critics. Opponents of the process object to using a human being as a "commodity" to serve a particular end. They also argue that these "designer babies" are the gateway to other uses of PGD, such as the elimination of disabilities or the creation of embryos with particular appearances. Yet the strongest critique comes from those ethicists who worry for the welfare of the savior siblings themselves. Will parents treat that second sibling differently? Will that child feel unwanted? Will that child be unwanted—merely a necessary inconvenience generated solely to save a beloved first child? Britain's Daily Mail poignantly quoted one such seven-year-old savior sibling, Jamie Whitaker, who said of his role in saving his brother's life, "I know I was born to do that instead of being just born for me."

Existing siblings who are not matches may also experience jealousy or guilt. In the case of Gary, Harriet and Arthur do not blunt their motives. They do not want a second child, merely a savior for the first. However, the neighbors do want a child. In that way, the situation seems not unlike many other open adoptions or surrogate births. Whether or not the savior sibling could be forced to donate in this case, should the neighbors renege, is a harder question. Similarly, the issue would prove more difficult if the savior sibling faced a greater risk or significant medical consequence—as might occur if the second child were conceived as a potential kidney or cornea donor. It is hard to imagine a couple with a blind child and a sighted child, for example, being permitted to transfer a cornea from the latter to the former. No such concerning context appears to arise regarding Harriet and Arthur's bone-marrow-transplant goals.

People have children for all sorts of reasons—some noble and others base. For the most part, the state does not look into the motives of prospective parents. A case can be made that a doing so for couples who seek PGD to create savior siblings is somewhat arbitrary.

27

"We Want a Deaf Baby"

JIM AND JANICE are a deaf couple living in a large Midwestern city. Janice has been deaf since birth, while Jim lost his hearing as a result of meningitis at age two. The pair are both active members of the local deaf community. They have a deaf daughter, Abigail, who is nine years old.

When considering a second pregnancy, Janice undergoes genetic testing and learns that she carries a gene mutation that means any child she conceives will have a 50 percent chance of being born deaf. The couple then visits a fertility specialist in order to have a baby through in vitro fertilization (IVF). They request that the doctor use preimplantation genetic diagnosis to separate out the embryos with the hearing-loss mutation, and that the doctor implant one of these embryos, thereby ensuring that they will have a deaf child. "We want to preserve our deaf culture," explains Janice. "Deafness is part of our family's lifeblood."

Should the doctor implant a deaf embryo intentionally, rather than a hearing one, so that the couple have a deaf baby?

—∽—

REFLECTION: **Reproductive
Technologies and Disability**

DEAF CULTURE REFERS to a series of traditions, social norms, and values embraced by individuals with varying degrees of limited hearing acuity. Many members of the deaf community do not consider their deafness to be a disability at all. For them, having a child who can share their distinctive culture is an asset, not a liability. Similar reasoning is used by some deaf couples to reject cochlear implants for their children. What complicates this scenario is that Jim and Janice want to use modern reproductive technologies to create a child who exhibits a condition that many nondeaf individuals do view as a disability. If one accepts their choice, one must then explain how the case differs from a deaf couple who give birth to a hearing infant but, wanting a deaf child, ask the physicians to sever nerves in her ears to render her deaf. The moral distinction between choosing to create a deaf embryo or painlessly deafening an infant is somewhat arbitrary, often resorting to the fallacy of appealing to nature, and is generally hard to defend philosophically. At the same time, many people viscerally react to the cases differently—and the law clearly views the latter sort of intervention as a form of child abuse. There is no way of knowing in advance whether any particular child would be better served with or without the selected trait. One cannot wait until the child turns eighteen and then take her hearing away, nor can one deny the child hearing until age eighteen and then restore it.

In 2008, a deaf British couple, Tomato Lichy and Paula Garfield, who already had a deaf child, sought to use IVF to select for a second deaf child from a mix of deaf and hearing embryos. Parliament responded by passing the Human Fertilisation and Embryology Act 2008, which prevents using reproductive technologies to select for an embryo with a "serious physical or mental disability." Whether deafness qualifies as a serious disability remains an open question. (Of note, Lichy and Garfield ended up having a second daughter the old-fashioned way; by chance, she is also deaf.) In the United States, such selection is generally unregulated. One can imagine that few physicians would agree to select for an embryo that all would agree was severely disabled or carried a serious disease— such as intentionally implanting an embryo with a higher risk of cancer. Yet if society were to accept deafness as a legitimate trait for selection, one could make similar cases for blindness, dwarfism, and a host of other traits that threaten to limit the offspring in some manner.

28

Who Owns That Embryo?

GLENN AND GILLIAN, a married couple in their thirties, use in vitro fertilization to have a son, Frank. As they do not believe that destroying embryos is ethical, the pair arranges to have the other two embryos created through the IVF process frozen and stored in a special facility. They have not yet decided whether they wish to have more children. If not, they have informally discussed donating the extra embryos to other couples in need.

After twenty years of marriage, Glenn and Gillian divorce bitterly. Gillian, now in her late forties and past menopause, wishes to use the other embryos to have children on her own. "I absolve you of all responsibility and all child support," Gillian tells Glenn through her lawyer. Glenn is unwilling to consent to Gillian's using the embryos. He has already remarried and fathered another child. "Two kids are enough for me. More than enough," he responds. Glenn and Gillian never addressed—orally or in writing—what was to be done with the embryos if they divorced, nor is there any clear rule in their state that applies to such cases. A family court judge is assigned to decide the matter—and she is determined to "do the right thing" in this case.

Should the judge award the embryos to Gillian?

REFLECTION: Embryo Custody

MODERN REPRODUCTIVE TECHNOLOGIES have resulted in an estimated one million frozen embryos in storage in the United States. Unlike in some other countries that have set limits for the amount of time embryos can be stored, US law allows these entities to be preserved indefinitely. What is to be done with these embryos—which some view as potential life and others as property—poses a quandary, especially when divorcing parties disagree. These issues gained national headlines in the United States in 2015 when Nick Loeb, the ex-fiancé of Modern Family actress Sofia Vergara, penned a New York Times column making his case for custody of two embryos the couple had created prior to their split.

One key factor in assessing these disputes is whether couples have a written agreement determining how to handle embryos in case they part ways. (Loeb and Vergara apparently did have such an agreement—one that favors Vergara's position). While some states, most notably New York, have honored preconception agreements, it is not clear that all states will do so. By comparison, a parent cannot enforce a binding prenuptial contract regarding custody of a child, as children are not treated as property to be transferred at will. Despite this legal uncertainty, most fertility clinics now require clients to sign such directives.

At least ten cases have addressed this issue in US courts since 1992, when in Davis v. Davis, the Tennessee Supreme Court ruled that disputed embryos were neither persons nor property but belonged to an "interim category that entitles them to special respect because of their potential for human life." A majority of these cases were decided in favor of the parent who opposed bringing the embryos in question to term. In several other cases, the winning parent was a mother who had undergone chemotherapy resulting in infertility; implanting stored embryos was her only way to become a biological parent.

Lawyer Heidi Forster Gertner, one of the leading experts in the field of embryo custody, has identified certain trends in these cases: Courts generally honor advance written agreements between partners, while in the absence of such an agreement, judges favor the right not to reproduce over the right to reproduce. One exception to this general trend favoring nonparenting occurs in cases where one partner can no longer reproduce biologically in any other way, in which case her parenting rights are given priority. A distinction should also be noted between these cases, in which one of the partners wishes to raise the child herself, versus a hypothetical scenario in which a partner, motivated by religion, seeks to donate the embryos to a third party for so-called "embryo adoption." One suspects that courts will prove far less sympathetic to parties seeking to "adopt out" stored embryos.

In Glen and Gillian's case, Gillian's inability to procreate through other means might be given considerable consideration in deciding this dispute. At the same time, although she has personally absolved Glenn of responsibility and child support, state law might still hold him liable for the upkeep of these additional children—especially if these children were ever to rely upon public assistance.

29

Privacy Invasion or Child Protection?

A MIDWESTERN STATE is very concerned about the number of children born to cocaine-addicted mothers. While fears of prenatal cocaine exposure received much attention during the 1980s, and were probably overblown, cocaine use by pregnant women can result in babies with significant birth defects. Moreover, children raised in homes where cocaine is used run a higher risk of exposure to violence.

To deter such behavior, the state wants every newborn baby to be tested for cocaine in the bloodstream. The state asks hospitals to turn over the results, intending to place infants found to have cocaine in their bloodstream in foster care and to charge their mothers with the misdemeanor of child endangerment. However, the state's request is not legally binding, and doctors are permitted discretion regarding whether or not to turn over these test results.

Should physicians turn over these test results to the authorities?

REFLECTION: Punishing Prenatal Conduct

MANY ACTIVITIES OF pregnant women may have an impact on fetal life or health. Alcohol exposure in utero can cause intellectual disabilities. Smoking cigarettes can lead to miscarriages and underweight babies. The use of common pharmaceuticals can result in devastating birth defects. High-risk behaviors, such as motorcycle riding and mountain climbing, may also increase the likelihood of fetal injury. The government has generally sought to inform pregnant women of various potential threats, allowing them to make their own determinations about risk. Of course, all of these activities are legal. In contrast, some state governments have severely penalized women whose use of illicit drugs, most often cocaine, has allegedly led to injury or the death of the fetus.

In 2014, the New Republic reports that sixteen states currently treat in utero exposure to illicit drugs as a form of child abuse; fourteen require physicians to report such use. Several states, most notably South Carolina, have prosecuted women for exposing fetuses to cocaine. In 2001, Regina McKnight was convicted of homicide and sentenced to twelve years in prison for delivering a stillborn fetus after using the drug.

Advocates for such laws argue that exposing a fetus to potentially deleterious drugs is no different from other forms of child abuse. Surely, nobody would object to prosecuting a parent who allowed her one-year-old to snort cocaine or to shoot heroin. The purpose of laws such as South Carolina's is to prevent children from suffering the often-devastating consequences of exposure to various illegal substances. Yet critics of such laws argue that mothers like Regina McKnight are suffering from addiction, a medical condition, and are being punished for their inability to refrain from drug use. Opponents also note that these rules fall most heavily upon impoverished women and racial minorities, and that prosecutorial discretion often shields middle- and upper-class mothers from similar charges. A genuine concern exists that if such laws were to become widespread and well-known, some pregnant women would forgo prenatal care entirely in an effort to avoid toxicology testing—undermining the welfare of the fetuses that the laws are intended to protect.

While the state may have the right to enact such laws, whether doctors should comply, in situations where they are afforded discretion, is another matter entirely. Physicians must weigh the benefit that reporting individual drug abusers would achieve against the systematic damage that such disclosure would wreak upon overall physician-patient trust. Some doctors might decide that disclosure is never worth the cost—that reporting addicted mothers is simply one of those requests which with doctors should never comply. Others might fear for the welfare of the particular infant in front of them and decide to protect that child at all costs, no matter what the long-term consequences for confidence in the medical profession.

30

"We're Waiting for a Sign from God"

THE PURIFIERS ARE a small religious sect. They number roughly sixty and follow their spiritual leader, a former insurance salesman turned self-styled prophet, in all matters. Among the beliefs of their leader, whom they call "His Holy Eminence," is the doctrine that newborn children should not be fed without a sign from God: Most infants are blessed with such a sign—which can range from a rainbow to a lightning storm—but some are not. Those who are not must not be fed.

In the recent past, three Purifier mothers have starved their infants to death; these women are currently awaiting trial. In all of these cases, the mothers went into hiding with their newborns shortly after giving birth to prevent the state from assuming custody. The state is concerned for the future babies of two Purifier women who are currently pregnant. One is six months pregnant; the other, seven months pregnant.

Should the authorities detain these women against their will in a prison hospital until they give birth in order to protect their future babies?

———∿∿∿———

REFLECTION: Preemptive Detention

AMERICANS ARE GENERALLY uncomfortable with the idea of detaining people preemptively for offenses they have not yet committed. Such preemptive or civil detentions are permitted only in rare circumstances and for compelling reasons. For instance, courts have upheld the decision not to grant bail to criminal defendants deemed likely to offend again—even if they pose no flight risk and have not yet been convicted of crimes. Some states continue to hold convicted sex offenders under civil commitment statutes after they have served their criminal sentences, on the grounds that they pose an ongoing danger to the public. In general, however, arresting suspects before they have committed offenses is anathema to US jurisprudence. Similarly, most ethicists and legal experts reject the idea of detaining a pregnant woman involuntarily to impose better prenatal care.

At least one US state has attempted to confine pregnant women who it believes pose a danger to their future babies. In a well-publicized Massachusetts case in 2000, prosecutors sought to detain Rebecca Corneau, a member of a religious sect known as "The Body" (and derisively, in the media, as "the Attleboro Cult"). Corneau had been implicated in the starvation of a previous newborn, purportedly at the behest of sect leader Roland Robidoux, and the district attorney's office said it feared for the welfare of her fetus. A district court judge, Kenneth P. Nasif, ordered Corneau confined at a medical facility for the duration of her pregnancy. This decision prompted an outcry from women's rights advocates. Lynn Paltrow, the founder of the National Advocates for Pregnant Women, told Salon, "We don't arrest somebody because in the future they might commit some crime. We do not arrest or imprison people because a local prosecutor has a suspicion—without a trial and without enough evidence to even bring criminal charges. That's not supposed to happen in our society." Yet an appeal failed on technical grounds, and Corneau eventually gave birth in detention. The state immediately assumed custody of her newborn.

Clearly, the government should strive to impose the least restrictive means possible to protect Purifier children from neglect or injury. A case could be made for using tracking devices, like ankle monitors, to keep tabs on the whereabouts of these women prior to delivery. In light of the circumstantial evidence, the state might also consider monitoring these women carefully, after they give birth, to ensure their parenting is appropriate. Few ethicists would argue for outright detention as a first step, even if this approach proved easier and less costly than other measures. The sacrifice of liberty strikes many as too extreme. At the same time, at least one prominent judge, ruling in the most high-profile case to date on the subject, has determined that extreme circumstances do merit forcible confinement—so the future of such preventive detentions remains an open question.

31

"That Woman Stole My Sperm"

JOAN IS A nursing assistant in a fertility clinic. One afternoon, a man named Mr. Schroeder visits the clinic to provide sperm that will be used to inseminate eggs harvested from his wife for in vitro fertilization. Joan, who has a history of mental illness, sneaks into the storage locker later that evening and inseminates herself with a sample of Mr. Schroeder's sperm. Several months afterward, when she is certain that she is pregnant, she writes a letter to Mr. Schroeder, explaining how she became pregnant with his child and asking him to leave his wife for her.

Mr. Schroeder is deeply upset by this situation and hires an attorney. Rather than suing for damages—which are not particularly important to him—he sues to compel Joan to obtain an abortion. "This is a unique case," his lawyer informs the judge. "This is not a situation in which a man had sex and later regretted it. My client and this woman are total strangers. It is not reasonable for my client to be forced to become a biological parent under these circumstances." Abortion is legal at this point in Joan's pregnancy, but Joan, who is now under arrest, insists that abortion is immoral.

Do the unusual circumstances of this case justify ordering Joan to undergo an abortion?

~~~

REFLECTION: Forced Abortion

PROSPECTIVE FATHERS ARE generally permitted no decision-making authority in the United States with regard to the termination of pregnancies. As a result of the Supreme Court's decision in Planned Parenthood v. Casey (1992), both "spousal notification" and "spousal consent" requirements have been declared "undue burdens" on women's reproductive rights that violate the Constitution. This decision aligned US law with that of much of the developed world. (Some nations, including Japan and Turkey, still do require spousal authorization in most circumstances.) As Brooklyn Law School professor Marsha Garrison told the New York Times in 2005, "that embryo is in the woman's body, it's within her and can't be separated from her, so it's not just her decision-making about whether to bear a child, it's about her body." However, the fatherhood rights movement continues to advocate for a paternal role in abortion decisions, noting that men are often saddled with costs and responsibilities related to parenthood. In a controversial 1998 journal article, "The Male Abortion," attorney Melanie G. McCulley contends that men deserve the equivalent of abortion—namely, the right not to parent. She argues for a father's prerogative to sever all legal ties, including financial responsibilities, to a fetus prior to birth. An alternative variant of "male abortion" would allow for enforcement of preintercourse contracts that absolve men of financial obligations if they make their preference for abortion clear prior to the conception of any unwanted embryo. Critics note that such an approach might grant increased autonomy to men but would leave many children without adequate means of support.

In circumstances where men and women have had sex or sexual contact, courts have nearly uniformly refused to force abortions or to absolve men of parenting duties. In Salon, journalist Cathy Young catalogued several of these cases, which include: male victims of statutory rape, including a twelve-year-old boy molested by his babysitter; a man raped while intoxicated; and a man whose sperm was retrieved from a condom after oral sex and used for insemination with a syringe. In the words of Marsha Garrison, courts have taken the position that "if you engage in sexual intercourse, you assume the risk that a child will be born." The scenario involving Joan and the stolen sperm raises the question of whether the same set of rules should apply in cases where no sexual or social contact has occurred.

On rare occasions, courts do order abortions. For instance, cognitively impaired women may have abortions, even if they cannot meaningfully consent, if a judge determines that the termination is in their best interests. In 2014, a British family court did just that with a thirteen-year-old-girl who had an IQ of 54. In Massachusetts, probate judge Christina L. Harms ordered an abortion for thirty-two-year-old Mary Moe, a woman with schizophrenia, at the behest of her parents. (The decision was later overturned on appeal.) Surrogate motherhood contracts also often contain "abortion clauses," requiring termination in cases of birth defects or on the say-so of the hiring couple. During the 2012 presidential campaign, candidate Mitt Romney's son, Tagg, gained notoriety for including such a clause in his own surrogacy contract, despite his vocal anti-abortion views—a decision Tagg's lawyer later claimed was an error. However, it appears unlikely that these agreements are enforceable. A couple may be able to use such a clause to avoid payment but not to have a fetus terminated over the gestational carrier's objections.

If one views all abortions as immoral, of course, Mr. Schroeder does not have a compelling case to demand an abortion. However, if one views only forced abortions as wrong, Joan's case may be the rare exception to this general principle. One can compare the situation to another in which Joan stole Mr. Schroeder prized possession—maybe a priceless gemstone—and had the pilfered item surgically implanted beneath her skin. Would you allow forced surgery to retrieve this stolen item? If so, and you have no ethical objection to abortion per se, a strong argument can be made for forcing Joan to "turn over" the fetus she stole from Mr. Schroeder—Joan's own purported ethical objections to the procedure notwithstanding.

32

"I Won't Have a C-Section"

AMBER, A SINGLE twenty-two-year-old woman, is a professional bikini model. She decides to have a baby on her own—and has a series of flings with various ex-boyfriends in order to conceive a child. She does not know which of these men is the father of the fetus and does not want to know; in fact, she does not tell any of them that she is pregnant.

Amber is clear with her obstetrician that she will absolutely not have a Cesarean section. When the obstetrician explains that some C-sections are medically necessary, she scoffs and says, "You cut me, and I'll sue your pants off." As a result, she is "fired" by a series of ob-gyns until she learns not to mention C-sections at the first meeting. She decides to wait to tell her new ob-gyn, Dr. Chandler, until she is ready to deliver.

Unfortunately, nine months into the pregnancy, and only days from Amber's due date, the fetus develops severe complications. Without an immediate C-section, the fetus will likely die. Amber refuses to consent. "No baby is worth a scar," she tells Dr. Chandler. There is not enough time to bring the matter to a court for adjudication.

Should Dr. Chandler perform the C-section without Amber's consent?

———⟞∿∿⟝———

REFLECTION: Involuntary Cesareans

CASES OF WOMEN refusing medically indicated Cesarean sections are relatively rare. Most cognitively intact mothers want their babies to survive—and are usually willing to make sacrifices, such as undergoing surgery, to do so. Yet C-sections are not benign procedures: even in otherwise healthy women, the mortality rate (13.3 maternal deaths per 100,000 births) for such surgical deliveries is more than three times that for vaginal deliveries. In addition to cosmetic concerns, such as Amber's, a prospective mother might have legitimate medical worries about what amounts to a major potentially life-threatening operation.

Although forced C-section cases raise issues similar to those that arise when discussing elective abortion, many commentators have noted several distinctions between the two. While the burden of carrying a fetus to term may be significant, it is arguably not nearly as weighty as undergoing major surgery against one's wishes. In cases like Roe v. Wade, the mother's intent is generally to terminate fetal life. In contrast, many involuntary C-section disputes involve mothers who very much want their babies to survive—they just disagree with medical opinions or have a more elevated threshold for risk. In fact, in several high-profile cases during which doctors fought in court for

C-sections and lost, the mothers eventually delivered healthy babies. In Amber's case, one might ask whether "the fetus will likely die" means a 60 percent chance or a 99 percent chance of demise. Assuming one believes society has some stake in fetal life beyond a certain point of development, one must decide at what point the risk to the full-term fetus becomes elevated enough that the decision-making power should be transferred from the mother to the state. One might also ask whether Amber's motivation matters. If she objected on medical or religious grounds, rather than cosmetic ones, would that change the case?

Many bioethicists are uncomfortable with the idea of forcing a competent patient to undergo surgery, no matter how compelling the reason. Howard Minkoff, OB-GYN chair at Maimonides Medical Center in Brooklyn, gave voice to these concerns regarding the case of Rinat Dray, who claimed that doctors at Staten Island University Hospital forced her into a C-section. Minkoff told the New York Times, "In my worldview, the right to refuse is uncircumscribed. I don't have a right to put a knife in your belly ever." Major professional organizations, including the American Academy of Pediatrics and the American College of Obstetricians and Gynecologists, generally discourage forced surgery, except under extraordinary conditions. No legal consensus yet exists regarding how to handle these challenging cases, and courts in different states have reached highly divergent opinions. For example, judges in Georgia and Florida have upheld forced C-sections, while Illinois's courts have proven unwilling to do so.

33

"Whose Fetus Is This?"

PERRY AND PATRICIA are a happily married couple. The one misfortune they have experienced is that Patricia suffers from a rare blood-clotting disorder that would make it dangerous for her to give birth. Since they desperately want to have children, the couple hires a surrogate mother, Thelma, who agrees to gestate the embryo they create via in vitro fertilization in return for a small cash payment and coverage of her healthcare costs. This arrangement is perfectly legal in their state.

Shortly before the baby is born, Perry and Patricia are murdered by the Zodiac Strangler. They have not made arrangements regarding who is to care for the child after their death. The reality is that Patricia's family lives overseas and is not interested in raising this child. However, Perry's mother, Beatrice, is very much interested in adopting the child. When a healthy baby boy is born, Beatrice demands that Thelma surrender the child to her. Thelma refuses. "I didn't have any agreement with you," she says. "I gave birth to him, and since Perry and Patricia are dead, he's mine." The two parties refuse to agree to a joint custody arrangement.

Assuming both Beatrice and Thelma would be excellent parents, who has a better claim to the child?

***

REFLECTION: Surrogacy after a Homicide

TRADITIONAL SURROGATE MOTHERHOOD involves artificially inseminating the surrogate with the prospective father's sperm. Gestational surrogacy, which has become far more common in the United States, entails implanting a previously conceived embryo in the surrogate's womb. This embryo may be the biological product of the intended parents, or the parents may use a donor for sperm, egg or both. In traditional surrogacy, the surrogate is both the genetic and biological mother of the child. In gestational surrogacy, which is the method that Perry and Patricia have chosen in the scenario, Thelma is not the genetic mother. Which form of surrogacy a couple uses may have significant legal consequences and ethical implications.

The first traditional-surrogacy contract in the United States was written by attorney Noel Keane in 1976, while the first gestational surrogacy occurred in 1985. Around the same time, the issue gained national prominence when a legal controversy erupted around a newborn known to the public as Baby M. This case originated from a traditional surrogacy contract between a New Jersey woman, Mary Beth Whitehead, and prospective parents Bill and Betsy Stern. Shortly after giving birth to a baby girl—whom Whitehead named Sara and the Sterns called Melissa—Whitehead asserted her intention to keep the child. A two-year legal battle led the New Jersey Supreme Court overturned the surrogacy contract on public policy grounds. (The Sterns were awarded custody anyway, under the "best interest of the child" standard.)

Over the following decades, states have diverged greatly in their approaches to surrogate motherhood. California and New Hampshire, known as surrogacy-friendly states, permit commercial contracts, while New York allows only altruistic (uncompensated) surrogacy. Michigan—among the least surrogacy-friendly states—not only refuses to enforce such contracts, but provides significant criminal penalties for entering into one. Many foreign countries also forbid surrogacy contracts, leading to a rise in so called "fertility tourism" to nations with surrogacy-friendly laws. India and Thailand were leading destinations for Western couples until those nations banned commercial surrogacy to foreigners in 2015.

The relationship between surrogates and intended parents can prove complex, especially under trying or tragic circumstances. Conflict may arise over how to handle fetuses with severe defects or disabilities. While some surrogacy agreements contain clauses requiring termination in cases of severe abnormalities, it remains unclear whether these are enforceable. In a high-profile 2012 case, surrogate Crystal Kelley refused a payment of $10,000 to abort a fetus with significant deformities; eventually, she fled from Connecticut to Michigan to avoid enforcement of her surrogacy contract. A British couple made headlines in 2014 when they refused to take custody of a baby girl from a surrogate because the child had been born with congenital myotonic dystrophy, a debilitating genetic disorder—a decision which was perfectly legal in Great Britain. (The couple did claim the baby's healthy twin brother as their own.)

Most jurisdictions that recognize surrogacy vest all of the rights of parenthood upon the intended parents from the moment that surrogacy begins. The surrogate generally retains no such rights. In scenario involving Beatrice and Thelma, the deaths of Perry and Patricia are unlikely to change that. Prior to the killings, Beatrice was expecting to become a grandmother and Thelma was planning to give up the child to whom she would give birth in return for compensation. Assuming Perry and Patricia's estate pays Thelma the agreed-upon fee and reimburses her for her hospital bills, one is hard-pressed to argue why their intervening deaths should alter the contract. Most states will allow the next of kin to assume care of the newborn of deceased parents, unless they have spelled out alternative preferences. An even more challenging case might arise if Perry and Patricia had no surviving family at all and Thelma was seeking custody of the child to prevent him from becoming a ward of the state. In an odd twist, she might find herself adopting the same child to whom she gave birth.

34

When Sterilization Is Forced

Maria is a fourteen-year-old girl with severe intellectual disabilities. Her IQ has been estimated between 35 and 40. When she begins menstruating, she finds the process severely traumatic and believes that she is bleeding to death. She sobs for hours, rocking back and forth in bed until her period ends. This occurs every month for nearly a year.

Her parents, Henry and Eliza, are reluctant to place her on a birth control regimen because there is a strong history of early-onset strokes in the family, a relative contraindication for oral contraceptives. Instead, they would like to have Maria's uterus and ovaries removed surgically. They believe this will serve her emotional well-being. However, the involuntary sterilization of those with cognitive impairments has a long and disturbing history in both Europe and the United States, so Maria's physician, Dr. Moreau, refers the case to a senior ethicist at the hospital for guidance.

Should Dr. Moreau be allowed to go ahead with the surgery?

REFLECTION: Eugenics in History

STERILIZATION OF THE mentally ill has had a controversial and often ugly history in the United States. Beginning in 1907, when Indiana first legalized the practice, until the 1970s, more than sixty thousand Americans were sterilized against their wills. This effort was part of a eugenics program that sincerely sought to improve the human species but relied largely on both faulty science and ethnic prejudices. Its most famous moment likely occurred in 1927, when in Buck v. Bell, the US Supreme Court upheld Virginia's sterilization program in a case involving a young woman named Carrie Buck. In an opinion that has tarnished his legacy, celebrated justice Oliver Wendell Holmes Jr. declared that "Three generations of imbeciles are enough." Holmes drew an analogy to military service, writing that "the public welfare may call upon the best citizens for their lives" and "it would be strange if it could not call upon those who already sap the strength of the State for these lesser sacrifices." Many years later, paleontologist Stephen Jay Gould investigated the circumstances surrounding Carrie Buck's sterilization and discovered that neither she nor the daughter she had prior to her sterilization were "feeble minded," as claimed by the state of Virginia. In 2013, North Carolina agreed to pay millions of dollars to compensate victims of its forced-sterilization program.

Any discussion of sterilizing Maria must occur against this grim historical backdrop. Some modern ethicists have argued that, in spite of this legacy, sterilization of those unable to consent should still be permitted when the benefits to the patient outweigh the costs. If individuals have the cognitive ability to consent to sterilization or to engage in parenting, the decision should be left to them; in cases where they do not, some argue that the welfare of the patient, or of both the patient and society, should be weighed in making such a decision. The American College of Obstetricians and Gynecologists does not automatically prohibit sterilization for impaired individuals but suggests the decision be made in consultation with the patients' parents and caregivers.

Critics of such an approach argue that there are some medical interventions that just should not be done, ever, despite the potential merits in certain circumstances. They often classify forcible sterilization as beyond a red line. Justice Holmes, in a different case, quoted the adage that "hard cases make bad law." By allowing sterilization in an extreme and emotionally charged case like Maria's, this critique charges, one establishes a precedent for similar action in cases that may prove more troublesome.

If one does believe that involuntary sterilization is sometimes permissible, though, it is hard to conceive of a more meritorious case than Maria's. Her menstruation is causing her personal, acute, and recurrent distress; other, lesser interventions are medically contraindicated; and her parents have advocated for the sterilization out of what appears to be a sincere concern for Maria's welfare. Other cases, alas, may prove even more fraught with complexity.

35

Paying for Girls

A SMALL WEALTHY nation faces a demographic challenge: as a result of infanticide and illegal sex-selective abortions, the number of males who live to adulthood is projected to exceed the number of females who do so by 15 percent within the next twenty years. This reflects a traditional preference for male heirs combined with technologies that enable couples to know the gender of their fetus in utero. The leaders of the nation fear this gender imbalance will lead to social unrest and widespread unhappiness.

To combat this problem, the national government decides to set up a state-sponsored program of "sperm sorting." Sperm sorting allows male sperm to be separated from female sperm prior to conception; the female sperm can then be used for artificial insemination, producing female babies. The process is not foolproof—but it is 70–80 percent effective. The country decides to offer sperm sorting for free to any couple willing to select a girl. These couples will also receive a payment of $10,000.

Is such a program ethical?

REFLECTION: Sex Selection

MANY WOULD-BE PARENTS throughout history have had gender preferences for their children. Until the second half of the twentieth century, these individuals had limited recourse. As every English schoolchild learns, King Henry VIII's desire for a male heir—and his limited understanding of reproductive biology—cost several royal wives their heads. Since the 1970s, however, various methods have been available to influence a child's sex. The first of these techniques, named after its developer, Ronald Ericsson, takes advantages of the differing "swim" speeds of male and female sperm. Sorting sperm by sex and then using artificial insemination reportedly achieves 69–75 percent success. Preimplantation genetic screening (PGS), which became widely available in the 1990s, affords much higher accuracy rates. A third approach, pioneered by Glenn Spaulding, uses flow cytometry to separate male and female sperm prior to conception—avoiding the destruction of embryos that accompanies PGS. The rise of affordable ultrasound technologies, which enable parents to know the gender of a fetus in advance, has also led to sex-selective abortions.

Gender preferences differ significantly by nation and culture. In the United States, data suggests a bias toward girls in couples using PGS—or, at least, among those who do select for gender. In contrast, a large swath of Asia—including China, India, South Korea, and Bangladesh—displays a preference for boys.

Economist Amartya Sen was the first to publicize the gender imbalance in these Asian nations resulting from a generation of "missing women": female victims of either gender-selective abortions or infanticide. (A competing hypothesis advanced by economist Emily Oster attributes the gender imbalance to the influence of endemic hepatitis B, but it appears to be less persuasive.)

Far from being only individual reproductive choices, parental gender preferences may have widespread societal implications. Psychologists and sociologists have linked this artificial gender imbalance (i.e., a population with an unnaturally elevated ratio of boys to girls) to political instability and violence, as large numbers of young males are unable to marry and start families. In Bare Branches: The Security Implications of Asia's Surplus Male Population, political scientists Valerie Hudson and Andrea den Boer have also suggested that the gender imbalance in China, and especially the preponderance of single low-status males, may threaten international security.

Some critics of sperm sorting will object to all efforts to tamper with so-called "natural" human reproduction. For many ethicists, context can shape the morality of reproductive choices. Using sperm sorting to create a male baby in China or India, where doing so exacerbates existing gender imbalances and contributes to underlying social problems, may be unethical. In contrast, a family who already has several girls in female-majority Russia or Hong Kong might harness the identical technology to have a boy for the purposes of gender balance without raising the same ethical concerns. Of course, as in the scenario presented, one might question the wisdom of paying anyone to have a child—either male or female—in a world already suffering from overpopulation and a shortage of resources.

36

Tube-Tied

AFTER BARBARA GIVES birth to her fourth child, she decides to have her "tubes tied" through a surgical tubectomy. Her husband, Oliver, fully supports her decision. Barbara enlists Dr. Crane, a well-regarded gynecologist, to perform the operation. Barbara returns home and—after waiting forty-eight hours, as instructed—resumes her vigorous sex life with her husband.

Approximately five weeks later, Barbara realizes that she is pregnant. As she and Oliver do not believe abortion to be ethical, she has no choice but to bring the fetus to term. Nine months after an operation to have her tubes tied, Barbara finds herself to be the mother of a lovely baby girl.

Barbara and Oliver sue Dr. Crane for malpractice. To their surprise, the physician acknowledges his mistake. "I looked at my notes," he says. "I seem to have tied only one tube." Where Dr. Crane disagrees with the couple is over the damages. He says, "I'll pay the medical costs for the pregnancy and for another tubectomy, and also a reasonable sum for their surprise—but let's face it, they're not really any worse off than they were before I operated. They have a beautiful child, don't they?" Barbara and Oliver insist that it is not nearly enough.

They want considerably more money, enough to offset the cost of raising their daughter from diapers through college.

Who has the better argument regarding the amount of damages owed?

REFLECTION: Wrongful Birth

THE LEGAL SYSTEM has long grappled with cases of individuals who benefit from an interaction, but sue anyway, claiming they did not benefit as much as promised. Such cases are particularly common in medical malpractice. In fact, one of the most famous cases in all of legal education—featured in the 1973 film, The Paper Chase—that of Hawkins v. McGee (1929)—involved a surgeon who promised a disabled patient a "perfect hand" but merely produced a functional one. That case, and many others, ask: Should one receive "expectation damages," based upon what one was promised, or only actual damages, measured by how much worse off one is? These issues are particularly challenging in scenarios of "wrongful birth" or "wrongful life"—the former referring to suits by parents on behalf of unwanted offspring, and the latter to those by the progeny themselves. These suits often involve severely disabled children whose doctors conduct inadequate preimplantation screening or negligently fail to diagnose disabilities prior to birth. They tap into complex philosophical questions, such as how one values existing with a crippling disability versus not existing at all.

Wrongful-life claims date back to at least the early 1980s. In the first case of its kind, Wrenn and James Turpin of California successfully sued the physicians who had failed to diagnose a genetic hearing defect in their older daughter until after their younger daughter was born. If the couple had known they carried the recessive genes that might lead to deafness, they argued in court, they would not have risked giving birth to a second daughter who also turned to be deaf. (This was technically a wrongful-life case because the couple sued on behalf of their child.) In a New Jersey case in 1984, the parents of Peter Procanik won a similar suit on the grounds that physicians had failed to recognize his mother's German measles, leading to his congenital rubella syndrome.

In response to these lawsuits, which some critics viewed as legitimizing abortion, a number of states passed statutes specifically prohibiting such claims. A Utah court even interpreted state law to protect doctors who intentionally withhold a fetal diagnosis to deter an elective abortion. Law professor Wendy Hensel has criticized such lawsuits as divisive to the disabled community and a "threat facing all individuals with disabilities."

How one feels about damages in these cases may depend, in part, upon one's view of the purposes of the medical malpractice system. If one sees damages as a way of making the victims "whole" again, then Barbara and Oliver may have a less persuasive case for large-scale compensation. Juries tend not to award much money to parents of healthy children, no matter how egregious the circumstances of their births. In contrast, if one considers the principle goal of the malpractice system to be punishing negligent physicians, in order to deter sloppy care, then a much stronger case can be made for making Dr. Crane (and his insurer) pay. If Dr. Crane's insurance premiums sky-rocket, one imagines that he would be more careful about tying tubes in the future.

37

When Human Cloning Becomes Possible

Dr. No, a well-regarded Ivy League philosophy professor, was the leader of a sect of devout atheists who followed his creed of skepticism and self-interest. He and his followers were interested in having him cloned, so that his successor might have his exact DNA, even though the technology to clone humans was not yet available. However, Dr. No arranged to have a sample of his DNA carefully preserved in case the technology was developed someday. He also identified several young women whom he wanted to bring his cloned embryos to term.

Eventually, Dr. No died. His followers remain deeply devoted to his beliefs. If scientists are able to develop the technology to clone humans, and one of these women is still willing to bring the clone to term, would it be ethical to fulfill the wishes of Dr. No and his followers?

———— ∿ ————

REFLECTION: Human Cloning

Although Aldous Huxley introduced readers to human cloning in 1932 in his novel Brave New World, where "Bokanovsky's

Process" produced batches of identical humanoids, the prospect of human reproductive cloning as a genuine scientific possibility did not arise until the 1960s. In the wake of British biologist John Gurdon's experiments transferring nuclei from frog cells into enucleated eggs, Nobel laureate James Watson penned an essay, "Moving Toward the Clonal Man," in the Atlantic Monthly in 1971 that placed the issue squarely on the public radar. Another twenty-five years elapsed before the cloning of Dolly the Sheep demonstrated that mammalian cloning was achievable in practice.

Whether human reproductive cloning is possible remains controversial, but no successful attempt has been documented. Cypriot American biologist Panayiotis Zavos has claimed twice—in 2004 and 2009—to have cloned and implanted human embryos, but has not provided evidence. South Korean veterinarian Hwang Woo-suk's claims to have cloned embryonic stem cells were retracted as fraudulent in 2005. About forty-six nations, including Great Britain, France, and Germany, have banned reproductive cloning. So have approximately fifteen US states. In 2009, President Barack Obama declared that reproductive cloning "is dangerous, profoundly wrong, and has no place in our society, or any society." However, inability to reach a consensus on the subject of "therapeutic cloning"—a related process in which cloned embryos are created for research or medicine, rather than brought to term—has prevented passage of a federal ban on cloning in the United States.

Critics of human reproductive cloning fall into two broad categories. One set of scholars objects to the practice in principle, arguing that it undermines human dignity—either that of the clone or that of human beings as a whole. These opponents note the potential that cloning has to undermine family life; with cloning, no genetic partner is needed to reproduce. They assert that every human being has "a right to his own genetic identity" (to quote the European Parliament's 1998 resolution against cloning). They also express the fear that clones will be created for "instrumental" purposes, such as to provide donor tissues or organs for their progenitors. Possibly the most vocal critic from this camp is Leon Kass, the chair of the President's Council on Bioethics under President George W. Bush, who wrote in 1997: "We are repelled by the prospect of cloning human beings not because of the strangeness or novelty of the undertaking, but because we intuit and feel, immediately and without argument, the violation of things that we rightfully hold dear." A second group of critics opposes reproductive cloning on more practical grounds. These opponents argue that there will be "clonism" (i.e., discrimination against clones) and that the process is fraught with risk for the potential clone— including serious disability and illness—citing the short, often disease-ridden lives of other cloned mammals. Until these difficulties can be resolved, they argue, cloning is a dangerous and unjust experiment.

Cloning is not without its intellectual partisans. University of Oxford philosopher Julian Savulescu, among the foremost of these defenders, argues that if the process can be perfected to resolve practical health concerns, reproductive cloning will represent "one of the greatest scientific advances" and will "signal a new kind of human relationship." He says that clonism need not be feared, because clones will prove no more or less human than anybody else.

This reality may turn out to be the greatest challenge to Dr. No's followers: The doctor's clones would share his identical DNA but would also be the product of an entirely different environment. They would not actually be him.

Finally, one should note that the fears over human reproductive cloning as a significant social force may be largely overblown. While members of a few small religious sects, like the Raëlians, seek to use reproductive cloning, polls show that the vast majority of people have absolutely no interest in having themselves cloned.

38

Bringing Up (Neanderthal) Baby

RESEARCHERS IN THE Alps have discovered the remains of a Neanderthal frozen and preserved in glacial ice there. With the help of fertility specialists, they are able to extract DNA from the sperm of this preserved prehuman. Their hope is to infuse his DNA into Homo sapiens sperm and use that sperm cell to fertilize a human egg. They have already recruited a female scientist who is willing to attempt to bring such an embryo to term in her womb.

Is it ethical for the researchers to move ahead with such a project?

REFLECTION: Animal Cloning

THE BIRTH OF Dolly the Sheep in July 1996 transformed animal cloning from science fiction into science fact. Since that time, researchers have successfully cloned pigs, dogs, cats, horses, rats, and a slew of other animals. The prospect of cloning human beings remains both scientifically challenging and, for many, ethically fraught. Until very recently, existing technologies did not allow for the cloning of extinct species, such as a Neanderthal, in which only fragments of DNA, rather than intact nuclei, exist. However, the development of genetic tools such as clustered regularly interspaced short palindromic repeats (CRISPR) may allow for creating a near approximation of such lost species by inserting their genes into cells of closely related living species. Harvard geneticist George Church has explained that once such DNA is reassembled inside a human cell, either a chimpanzee or an "extremely adventurous female human" might bring the clone to term. Church argues that a potential benefit to humans of such Neanderthal cloning would be increased genetic diversity. His book, Regenesis: How Synthetic Biology Will Reinvent Nature and Ourselves, ignited a widespread backlash among more risk-averse scientists.

Assuming the cloning of a Neanderthal to be possible, the decision to clone raises distinct ethical concerns. First, if researchers were to choose a female scientist to gestate the fetal prehuman, one must consider the health and safety implications for this individual. Since this experiment has never been done before, some risks and consequences may prove unforeseen. (It is worth noting that the US federal government has deemed pregnant women to be a vulnerable population requiring special safeguards when conducting research; one wonders how an institutional review board would address a situation in which the pregnancy itself was the experiment.) Are there some risks so great, one must ask, that no person can meaningfully consent to them voluntarily?

A second concern involves the welfare of society as a whole.

Who can say that the newly created Neanderthal will not be a source of disease or that the creature will not prove violent? While one Neanderthal might turn out to be relatively harmless, this experiment would likely lead to others, and there is no telling what damage hundreds or thousands of such creatures (or the offspring of human-Neanderthal mating) might do. Moreover, society has yet to generate a set of rules governing such creatures. Would they be treated as fully human? As animals akin to other primates? Would they be held criminally accountable for their actions? Eligible for public benefits? However one feels about cloning Neanderthals, most would agree that these are questions that should be resolved before cloning actually takes place.

Finally, any ethical assessment of Neanderthal cloning must consider the welfare of the individual being cloned. One might reasonably conclude that such a creature would face loneliness, discrimination, and a whole host of other psychological and social ills. Bringing an advanced Homo sapiens–like primate into the world merely to satisfy our own intellectual curiosity seems problematic. However, if a more compelling need arose—such as a decline in human genetic diversity that led to increased disease vulnerability—then the advantages would have to be weighed closely against the moral and practical hazards.

39

Fertility and Fundamentalism

BETSY AND TRIXIE are a married lesbian couple in their early thirties who are seeking to have a baby through in vitro fertilization; a male colleague of Betsy's has agreed to serve as a sperm donor, and Trixie plans to carry the baby to term. They schedule an intake appointment at Best Babies Ever Fertility Clinic, choosing the clinic because it was recommended by Betsy's cousin and has an excellent rating on Yelp.

When they arrive, they complete the initial paperwork, including a demographic survey and health questionnaire. They are then ushered into the office of Dr. Higgins, an experienced ob-gyn, who explains that she will not be able to offer IVF to the couple, because assisting nonheterosexual couples with artificial conception violates her religious beliefs. "It would be unfair to all of us and would not foster a healthy, honest physician-patient relationship," she explains. She states that she will be glad to refer them to a colleague, Dr. Sternin, who runs an excellent IVF practice fifteen minutes away.

Should Dr. Higgins be allowed to refuse Betsy and Trixie services under these circumstances?

REFLECTION: LGBTQ Rights

FOR THE LAST four decades, society has grappled with the challenge of balancing the religious liberties of physicians against the needs of prospective patients. In the 1970s, after the legalization of abortion, Congress passed legislation, known as the Church Amendment (after Frank Church, a Democratic senator from Idaho), preventing the government from forcing physicians and hospitals to offer abortion or sterilization. At the time, this "refusal clause" was largely uncontroversial, passing the Senate by a vote of 92–1. Since then, conflict has arisen around proposed so-called "conscience clauses" in some states that allow pharmacists to refuse to fill prescriptions for contraceptives.

One should note that laws regarding reproductive health and, more recently, assisted suicide, are exceptions to the general rule that hospitals and doctors-in-training must perform all standard procedures. It is highly unlikely that a Jehovah's Witness would be allowed to pursue a surgery residency if she agreed only to partake in "bloodless" operations or that a Scientologist would be permitted to train as a psychiatrist while opting out of the prescription of psychoactive medications. In the cases covered by the Church Amendment—as well as the subsequent Coates and Weldon Amendments—doctors were permitted to refuse to offer particular services to all people. More challenging are circumstances where providers deny service to some individuals, but not to others.

Betsy and Trixie may liken their situation to other forms of discrimination in the delivery of goods and services, such as the baker who refuses to make a gay couple a wedding cake or the lunch counter that denies service to African American customers. A noteworthy difference is that the interaction between baker and cake buyer is largely transactional, while doctors and patients—especially in the setting of reproductive health—often require close relationships based on mutual trust and respect. It is also worth noting that many people walk into a bakery or a lunch counter off the street and will likely suffer humiliation if discriminated against. IVF services are rarely an "impulse buy" and, in theory, a fair-warning system could be set up to help couples avoid seeking services at clinics that will not serve them. Yet knowing that one has to inquire whether a clinic serves people of one's sexual orientation may itself be humiliating and might stamp gays and lesbians with a badge of inferiority.

Whatever one ultimately decides about the permissibility of Dr. Higgins's behavior, one should recognize that the case can be analyzed in one of two ways. A decision can be rendered creating a blanket rule through which either religious freedom or healthcare equality always triumphs; alternatively, one might look at the actual impact on access. Will forcing Dr. Higgins to offer services to Betsy and Trixie lead to greater IVF availability for lesbians? Or will physicians like Dr. Higgins close their doors entirely—driving both gay and straight customers to other specialists, ultimately decreasing access to IVF for all.

The law remains very much unsettled in this area. In California, a long-running lawsuit between Guadalupe Benitez, a lesbian woman, and two religious physicians who refused her reproductive services, was ultimately decided by the California Supreme Court in favor of Benitez. In other states, some fertility specialists continue to refuse service to gay and lesbian couples.

PART FOUR

The Good of the Many

How to balance the welfare of individuals against the collective good has puzzled philosophers since antiquity. The European Enlightenment of the eighteenth century, drawing upon the writings of philosopher John Locke (1632–1704), prioritized personal liberty. While embracing many of the Enlightenment's values, utilitarian philosophers, including Jeremy Bentham (1748–1832) and John Stuart Mill (1806–1873), argued that individual welfare, on aggregate, could best be served by aiming for policies that achieve the greatest good for the greatest number of people. Meanwhile, early socialists—a wide swath of advocates for communitarianism, ranging from the utopian followers of Robert Owen (1771–1858) to the Bolshevik heirs, to Karl Marx (1818–1883), disparaged individualism as an impediment to collective action.

Arguments can be advanced for creating societies based upon the purest forms of any of these theories, but modern healthcare is a hybrid that reflects many competing values. One may favor expanded personal freedom, but in a system where nearly all citizens rely upon some form of public or private health insurance, individual decisions impact everyone's premiums and taxes. Utilitarian values may lead to better healthcare outcomes on the aggregate, but few of us would favor carving up randomly selected citizens for their organs—even if transplanting these organs could save a larger number of lives.

The very nature of contemporary society requires a complex, ever-evolving series of trade-offs between rights and duties and between the self and the community. Inevitably, as a result of chance and circumstances, some people are called upon to make greater sacrifices for the well-being of their neighbors than others. Historically, the burden has often fallen most heavily upon those with the least access to political power and social capital. Contemporary medical ethicist and policy makers often find themselves asking: How much sacrifice is too much to demand? And what if individuals refuse to cede rights or interests for the common good? As technology and globalization render the world more interconnected, the answers to these questions grow increasingly important—and often remain elusive.

40

Paid to Not
Have Kids

A NONPROFIT ORGANIZATION called the Infant Protection Service (IPS), wants to pay women who have been treated for substance abuse $1,000 monthly not to have children until they can demonstrate a year of sobriety. Many addictive drugs, such as alcohol and cocaine, increase the risk of birth defects, and parents who are addicted to drugs often have a hard time maintaining a safe, stable home environment for their children.

The organization wants to make the program available to all current and former patients of the Stone Cold Institute (SCI), a drug-and-alcohol rehabilitation program that serves low income residents of New York City. The nonprofit's staffers ask SCI to allow them to place posters in the facility's lobby. Those patients who see the posters and are interested will register with the Infant Protection Service and then will take both drug and pregnancy tests every month; those who test negative on both will receive $1,000.

Is such a program ethical?

REFLECTION: The Rights of Substance Abusers

ALTHOUGH PARTICULAR NARRATIVES related to pregnancy and addiction, such as that of the "crack baby," may have been exaggerated during the 1980s, few can doubt the serious economic and social cost of significant substance abuse during gestation. Alcohol consumption, for example, is the US's leading "preventable cause" of both intellectual disabilities and birth defects. Marijuana exposure in utero has been tied to breathing difficulties, poor eyesight, and psychiatric problems. While the frequency of congenital defects due to prenatal cocaine exposure remains in dispute, cocaine use during pregnancy is known to cause premature delivery and attention deficits in offspring. In addition, many addicts lose custody of their kids, relegating these children to foster care. Yet reproduction and parenting are widely regarded as fundamental rights in Western culture—and state efforts to restrict those rights, especially in light of the checkered legacy of the eugenics movement in the US, generally meet with disfavor from both ethicists and the public. As the saying goes, "You need a license to have a dog, but not to have a baby."

In 1997, California mother Barbara Harris—who had already adopted four children from a crack-addicted mother—set out to combat this problem. She founded an organization called Children Requiring a Caring Kommunity (CRACK), now known as Project Prevention, whose goal was to pay addicts not to reproduce. Initially, the group offered more money for sterilization via tubal ligation and vasectomy than for the use of long-term birth control, but under pressure, it now pays the same for those who use surgical means as those who opt for intrauterine devices or hormonal therapies.

Reactions to these efforts range widely. For instance, social worker Attilio Rizzo Jr., of Brookdale University Hospital and Medical Center, described the program to the New York Times as "a godsend" when it first appeared in New York, while the city of Albuquerque welcomed Harris's volunteers to its jails. In contrast, some advocates for the urban poor and minority women objected to the organization's efforts to target these populations. Lynn Paltrow, founder of National Advocates for Pregnant Women, told the Times in 2003, "What she's doing is suggesting there are certain neighborhoods where it is dangerous for some people to be reproducing. It suggests they are not worthy of reproducing. . . . The Nazis said if you just sterilized the sick people and Jews you would improve the economy." Similar controversy greeted Project Prevention when it spread to Great Britain in 2010.

Harris sees herself as a crusader against child abuse. Critics argue that she has chosen the wrong target: that she should improve the lives of these addicts or help them overcome their addictions, but not coerce them into not having children.

In the case of the Infant Protection Service, the nonprofit appears to be striving to find a balance between these two approaches. By paying women both to stay sober and to postpone pregnancy, it appears to be incentivizing sobriety in the short term in order to prepare these women for childbearing and rearing in the future. Of course, giving women prone to addiction $1,000 to remain sober may prove self-defeating. One cannot help wondering how many of IPS's beneficiaries would truly remain substance-free at the end of a year.

41

"They Tried to Make Me Go to Rehab"

CLAY SUFFERS FROM severe alcoholism. He has lost his job as an attorney, and his family will not speak to him unless he obtains treatment. He is living on the streets, where he uses the money that he panhandles from strangers to purchase liquor. He has been taken by ambulance to the emergency room on forty-two nights in the last three months after being found passed out on the sidewalks under the influence of alcohol. There he has slept off his intoxication and departed in the morning after telling the ER doctors that he plans to continue drinking.

On several occasions, he has suffered seizures and required expensive weeklong hospitalizations—paid for by the state's insurance program for the poor. Clay turns down referrals to alcohol rehabilitation programs and even a list of Alcoholics Anonymous meetings. He states: "I don't want to quit. I like drinking."

One of the physicians at the hospital, Dr. Martha Livingston, finds it frustrating that thousands of dollars of taxpayer money are squandered providing care to Clay. She wants the municipality to pass a law allowing chronic alcoholics—defined as anyone brought to the hospital intoxicated more than ten times in thirty days—to be forcibly sent to a three-month rehabilitation program.

Should the municipality enact such a law?

REFLECTION: Drug Court

ALCOHOL AND DRUG use are implicated in a significant portion of emergency room visits in the United States, including approximately half of all admissions to trauma centers. According to the US Department of Health and Human Services, more than two million such visits occur annually. Many of these visits are accounted for by chronic substance abusers, who present to hospitals repeatedly in states of intoxication. Their bills are generally either paid for by the taxpayers, through Medicaid, or swallowed as charity care by hospitals. Many insurers are permitted by state laws to refuse payment for alcohol-related emergency services.

Since 1989, when, at the height of the crack cocaine epidemic Florida's Miami-Dade County set up the nation's first "drug court," judges have increasingly relied upon diversion programs to force addicts into treatment. More than three thousand drug courts now exist. Proponents note that three-quarters of arrestees who complete mandatory rehab programs remain arrest-free for two years, saving taxpayers an average $6,744 per participant. In contrast, critics argue that these programs give judges the power to make medical decisions for patients—and that these decisions are often misguided, such as denying methadone maintenance to recovering heroin addicts. Whatever their merits or disadvantages, drug courts take action only in cases of individuals charged with criminal offenses such as drunk driving and dealing drugs. The chronic alcoholic like Clay generally does not fall under their jurisdiction.

More recently, several states have enacted laws to allow family members of chronic alcoholics and drug users to petition the courts to commit their loved ones to treatment. Kentucky's statute, Casey's Law, adopted in 2004, is named after twenty-three-year-old Casey Wethington, who died of a drug overdose. It allows for judges to mandate rehab at the request of friends or family for anyone "suffering from an alcohol and other drug abuse disorder [that] presents a danger or threat of danger to self, family, or others if not treated." The only caveat is that the petitioner must agree to pay for the costs of treatment. Similar legislation has been enacted in Ohio. Indiana's Jennifer Act of 2015 allows for involuntary civil commitment for substance abusers in cases of demonstrated "dangerousness" or "grave disability," but requires family or doctors to identify both a facility willing to accept the patient and a guaranteed source of payment. A number of other states allow more limited interventions, but the majority of states leave the families of addicts without recourse. Hospitals are generally powerless to act in the absence of interest on the part of family or friends—although many chronic substance abusers have no family or friends to advocate for them. In 2013, Australia's Northern Territory established a program, similar to the one advocated by Dr. Livingston in the case of Clay; mandatory rehab is now a possibility there for anyone taken into protective custody by police for alcohol intoxication three times during a two-month period.

Opponents of mandatory rehab worry about criminalizing a medical condition. Some also justify their opposition on the grounds of individual autonomy: If Clay does not want to stop drinking, what right does society have to force him into sobriety? Pleas for autonomy may prove less persuasive when the taxpayers are picking up the tab for his conduct. An alternative, more radical approach might allow Clay to continue drinking—but, after multiple warnings, to cut off his access to alcohol-related emergency services.

42

A Modern Typhoid Mary

A PREVIOUSLY UNKNOWN virus appears in a major US city one summer. In most patients, the symptoms resemble those of a bad flu—fever, headache, some nausea. But a small number of patients, especially young children, develop significant internal hemorrhaging. By August, city health officials have uncovered ninety-three cases, six of which have proven fatal. Why some people become seriously ill but most do not remains a medical mystery.

Public health workers trace the disease back to Sandra, a thirty-year-old day-care worker, who has had contact—direct or indirect—with all of these patients. It turns out that Sandra "carries" this rare, untreatable virus in her bodily fluids, although she herself is entirely asymptomatic. Even casual contact with an object which Sandra has touched over the past several weeks can lead to infection.

Doctors want the city to quarantine Sandra in a hospital room until a treatment can be devised. However, there is no timetable for researching such a remedy. In fact, none is even under development, since Sandra is the only person in the world who is known to carry the disease, and isolating her will likely remove the threat to everyone else. Not surprisingly, Sandra objects.

Is it ethical to quarantine Sandra, who has done nothing wrong, indefinitely?

———∾∾———

REFLECTION: Mandatory Quarantines

FEW IF ANY issues display the conflict between individual rights and the public welfare as starkly as that of mandatory quarantine. The term itself originates from the Italian quaranta giorni, reflecting the forty days that ships were isolated during the era of the Black Death, a European plague pandemic that lasted from about 1346 to 1353. In the United States, patients suffering from leprosy were isolated in "colonies," such as those at Kalaupapa, Hawaii, and Carville, Louisiana. During the yellow fever epidemics of the nineteenth century, victims were isolated in many US cities; one such episode forms the basis for the Bette Davis film Jezebel (1938). More recently, efforts to detain patients with drug-resistant tuberculosis and Ebola virus have garnered national headlines. From 1986 to 1994, Cuba forcibly confined patients with HIV to sanatoria. Large scale "group" or "collective" quarantines were enforced upon entire communities, such as the smallpox restriction imposed in sections of Muncie, Indiana, in 1893 and the seclusion of the Chinese population of San Francisco in 1900 due to exaggerated concern about plague.

However, the most celebrated case of quarantine is likely that of Mary Mallon (1869–1938), a.k.a. Typhoid Mary, an asymptomatic carrier of typhoid fever. Mallon, an Irish American kitchen worker, was kept in forced quarantine for twenty-three years on North Brother Island in New York City's East River. Her custody is recounted in historian Judith Walzer Leavitt's book Typhoid Mary: Captive to the Public's Health.

The United States allows forcible quarantine for the following diseases: cholera, diphtheria, tuberculosis, plague, smallpox, yellow fever, viral hemorrhagic fevers (e.g., Ebola), pandemic flu, and severe acute respiratory syndromes (SARS). Some of these diseases are easily treatable; others have a short incubation period. Few ethicists are seriously troubled by the short-term quarantine of genuinely contagious individuals. Most reasonable people would accept such quarantine for themselves voluntarily in order to protect the public. Far more troubling are the rare patients who require long-term isolation—whether because they are untreatable, asymptomatic carriers such as day-care worker Sandra or because they refuse to engage in necessary care.

In Sandra's case, she is being asked to withdraw entirely from society—in essence, to become a hospital-bound prisoner through no fault of her own. In theory, one might compensate quarantine patients for their inconvenience, such as a year spent in "tuberculosis jail," but no amount of money would likely induce most people to enter indefinite isolation.

If society expects Sandra to comply with this isolation for the public good, it also has an ethical duty to expend considerable effort and resources upon finding a treatment for her condition. How much should society spend? It is possible to estimate what amount Sandra's quarantine will save the public in healthcare costs and economic losses. A strong philosophical argument exists for spending all of those funds on trying to cure her, although political realities make such a vast expenditure, even if ethically appropriate, highly unlikely

43

Beyond 23andMe

A FEMALE HOSPITAL employee, Dahlia, has been the victim of a violent sexual assault inside a stairwell. She dies without regaining consciousness. Fortunately, special victims unit investigators have been able to obtain a DNA sample from her attacker's semen.

The authorities are aware that all staff, patients, and visitors to the hospital must either swipe their employee identification cards or display a picture ID at the entrance, which is photographed and recorded in the security logbook. In an effort to identify Dahlia's attacker, the police request the names and contact information of all male staff, patients, and visitors to the facility over a two-week period prior to the attack. While they cannot force these individuals to provide DNA samples, they plan to request a sample from each of them—and would take a closer look at the alibis of those who refuse to provide a cheek swab.

Is it ethical for the hospital to provide such data to the police?

REFLECTION: DNA Dragnets

THE FIRST DNA sweep, or DNA dragnet, occurred in Great Britain in 1987. Efforts by the Leicestershire police to find a two-time rapist and murderer led indirectly to the arrest of Colin Pitchfork, a twenty-seven-year-old baker who boasted of having submitted a false DNA sample during the course of the testing of more than four thousand local men. In 1996, Oklahoma authorities conducted an unsuccessful DNA dragnet to find the killer of aspiring ballerina Juli Busken (although her murderer was later identified and convicted on the strength of DNA evidence). While such dragnets are not yet commonplace in the United States, they have been used to address high-profile murders in Louisiana, Florida, Massachusetts, and elsewhere. These sweeps increase the likelihood of arresting the perpetrators of violent offenses such as the attack on Dahlia. Moreover, the results are extremely accurate at connecting alleged assailants to crime scenes. If the authorities find whoever murdered Dahlia, his arrest would both prevent him from striking again and, in theory, would deter others from committing such attacks.

DNA dragnets are not without significant privacy concerns. Laypeople depend upon law enforcement authorities to ensure that their DNA, once harvested, is stored safely and will not be used for purposes other than solving specific crimes. Should such sweeps become more frequent, incidents of mishandling may prove inevitable. Moreover, even when conducted with appropriate safeguards, DNA dragnets can unwittingly reveal long-hidden family secrets. Such was the case in Italy, where a dragnet searching for the killer of schoolgirl Yara Gambirasio led to an unexpected revelation of false paternity. Yet since the DNA stored by the FBI in what is known as the Combined DNA Index System (CODIS) contains different markers from those used by medical geneticists or commercial genealogy companies like 23andMe, it was long thought that linking dragnet DNA to other samples was impossible. In 2017, Michael Edge of Stanford University and his colleagues published an article in the Proceedings of the National Academy of Sciences that proved otherwise. They showed that CODIS samples could be correlated with those in other data sets—raising the concern that a privacy breach of dragnet-obtained DNA could lead to the exposure of genetic data related to medical risks.

Consensual dragnets may not be as "voluntary" as they appear, as those who refuse to give a DNA sample will likely be subject to extensive scrutiny, even though many plausible reasons other than guilt—from privacy concerns to fear of the police—might lead a law-abiding citizen to refuse to participate. In Dahlia's case, relying upon the hospital's access data complicates the situation even further. Most people generally believe their visits to hospitals, either as patients or as guests, to be private matters. If the public feared such data were being mined by the police, the result could be a chilling effect on the entire healthcare system. Sick people, concerned for their privacy, might delay seeking medical care. Friends and relatives might avoid visiting their hospitalized loved ones.

An analogy can be drawn to the "library records provision"

of the Patriot Act of 2001, which allowed the federal government to track access to library materials as part of its so-called "war on terror." until it expired in 2015. Advocates claimed the policy would capture terrorists. Critics charged it would deter the conduct of legitimate library users. Of course, if people were to fear that a rapist and murderer remained on the loose in the hospital, this concern would also be likely to chill their behavior.

44

Requiring a DNA Test

INFANTILE TAY-SACHS DISEASE is a rare genetic disorder of childhood that usually appears within the first sixth months of life and is almost always fatal by age five. Children born with the disease become blind, deaf, and paralyzed. Dr. Bovary, a pediatrician and the US surgeon general, is particularly interested in eradicating this scourge.

Tay-Sachs is what is called a recessive genetic disorder. In order to develop the disease, a baby must receive a defective gene from each of his parents. Dr. Bovary wants to institute mandatory genetic testing for everyone of reproductive age—conducted as a condition for receiving a driver's license, passport, or government ID card. The simple test involves a swab of the cheek and is without medical risks; the government will not test for any other diseases, and plans to destroy the samples after testing. People will have access only to their own results.

"What people do with this information is entirely up to them," says Dr. Bovary. "They can choose partners who don't have the defective gene. They can choose not to have children. They can adopt. They can abort. They can even have babies with the disease, if they so choose. All I'm asking is that people know whether their potential children are at risk."

Is such a mandatory testing program ethical?

REFLECTION: Mandatory Genetic Screening

SCREENING OF NEWBORNS for genetic disease has occurred since the 1960s, when the first protein-based tests for phenylketonuria emerged. As of 2018, every state offers some form of disease-testing program for infants, and forty-eight of these programs are mandatory, although forty-three states permit parents to opt out under certain circumstances. The diseases covered vary. Most are treatable with immediate or early intervention. Much of the funding for screenings comes from the federal government through the Newborn Screening Saves Lives Reauthorization Act of 2014. These screening programs generally draw blood samples from newborns' heels; the blood has historically been stored for research purposes. A campaign against such sampling, led by Minnesota activist Twila Brase, has drawn national attention. Brase is concerned that, in the future, such blood samples may be used to predict gene-based character traits, such as a propensity for violence, which she views as a threat to privacy and parental autonomy.

For many newborns, genetic testing arrives too late. Infants afflicted with Tay-Sachs disease are without medical recourse. The only way to avoid the suffering inherent in the disease, according to mandatory screening advocates is to prevent these children from being born or conceived in the first place. Voluntary genetic-testing programs for prospective parents are widespread, such as the much-touted Dor Yeshorim, which means "Upright Generation," that serves Orthodox Jews, who happen to be among the groups with a high incidence of Tay-Sachs disease. Since 2004, Saudi Arabia has mandated health checkups for betrothed couples, and claims that 165,000 participants have broken off engagements as a result of genetic incompatibilities—but the true extent of genetic testing in that nation is unclear.

In the United States and western Europe, strong resistance to mandatory testing exists. Among opponents are some disability rights advocates, who fear a slippery slope that would lead to testing for blindness or autism, and libertarians, who raise broader concerns about privacy, autonomy, and even eugenics. These opponents often see a thin line between informing people of their genetic status and forcing them to make certain reproductive choices—like not having children or not mating with others who share their genetic defects. If most couples choose not to have infants with genetic diseases, they say, those who do have them will likely face social stigma. Others fear testing will increase abortion rates. Even for many bioethicists who favor abortion rights, choosing whether or not to have a child with a particular disease may be viewed as highly controversial. Emily Rapp's memoir The Still Point of the Turning World describes her deeply meaningful relationship with her son, Ronan, before his death from Tay-Sachs in 2013.

Supporters of mandatory testing generally advocate for

discrete, circumscribed programs looking for specific diseases like Tay-Sachs. Some note that the stigma surrounding having a baby with a debilitating, universally terminal disease may well be appropriate—if such an outcome can easily be avoided. Some bioethicists go as far as describing that choice as a form of child abuse, noting that no parent would ever be permitted to inflict similar symptoms on an infant after birth.

45

"I'd Rather Die Than Abandon My Hunger Strike"

THE INMATES AT a maximum-security prison have gone on a hunger strike to protest their living conditions. They claim overcrowding, chronic mistreatment by corrections officers, and a recent ban on tobacco. After six weeks forgoing food, one of the prisoners, Tony, is so nutrient-deprived that he may die without nutritional intake. Tony is awake and alert, and states, "I'd rather die than abandon my hunger strike." He adamantly refuses to accept artificial nutrition.

Is it ethical for the prison doctor to sedate Tony and then "feed" him through a nasogastric tube that would allow nutrients to be pumped directly into his stomach?

REFLECTION: Force-Feeding Prisoners

HUNGER STRIKES HAVE been used by protesters and prisoners for centuries, including celebrated fasts by female suffragettes in the early twentieth century, Mahatma Gandhi during the struggle for Indian independence, and Irish Republicans in

1981. Prisoners often have minimal autonomy, and threatening self-starvation is one of the few means of civil disobedience available to them. Many Americans are aware that the US government forcibly fed so-called "enemy combatants" detained at Guantanamo Bay during the 2000s. Far fewer realize that similar techniques are used against ordinary prisoners in the US criminal justice system. Although the issue drew some public attention in 2013 when US District Court judge Thelton Henderson granted prison doctors in California the authority to force-feed hunger striking convicts, the face of the movement against such force-feeding for years was Connecticut inmate Bill Coleman. Coleman, who refused food to protest what he believes was an unjust rape conviction, was strapped down regularly for involuntary tube feeds from 2008 to 2014. His strike ultimately ended when he was deported to his native England at the conclusion of his sentence.

Advocates for the legitimacy of force-feeding make two distinct sets of claims: First, they advance the welfare of the individual inmate. Society, they argue, has a right to prevent suicide—and inmates who refuse food are merely engaged in prolonged attention-seeking suicide attempts. Even if self-starvation were permitted outside of prisons, inmates are an inherently vulnerable population whose very capacity to make their own decisions about such high-stakes matters as suicide are necessarily diminished. In the interest of the inmates themselves, doctors have a moral obligation to preserve their lives. Second, force-feeding advocates claim that preventing such hunger strikes is essential for maintaining order in a complex and often dangerous penal system. Allowing inmates to starve themselves undermines the authority of corrections officials and places both prisoners and staff in danger.

Yet force-feeding, especially when the patient resists, is not a benign procedure. Both the American Medical Association and the World Medical Association have condemned the practice, which many human rights advocates regard to be a form of torture. Most medical professional organizations prohibit their members from participating.

Analogies are often drawn to the role of physicians in capital punishment. While doctors have dual loyalties, serving both patients and society, any significant entanglement of healthcare providers with law enforcement should require compelling justification. Even if one believes that force-feeding or the death penalty is itself ethical, it does not necessarily follow that physicians should have a role.

46

Nonvaccinators in the Waiting Room

DR. LIZ WILSON is a pediatrician in private practice. Among her patients is Ricky, the one-year-old son of Adeline and Roger. Up to the age of twelve months, Ricky has received all of his scheduled vaccinations. Yet when he arrives for his one-year well-child visit, Adeline informs Dr. Wilson that she does not want Ricky vaccinated for measles. "I've read online that the vaccine can cause autism," she says. "And anyway, the risk is so low. Why put all of those toxins in his tiny body for nothing?" Neither Adeline nor Roger cannot be persuaded to change their minds.

Dr. Wilson has learned that several measles cases have been recorded in her city that summer and at least one patient died. She is concerned that Ricky may become infected and then will expose her other patients—including those too young or too sick to be vaccinated—to measles.

Would it be ethical for her to tell Roger and Adeline that she can no longer treat their son?

~~~

REFLECTION: Parental Dissent

WHILE SOME DECISIONS by parents are so unreasonable that the law lets courts intervene, all states recognize at least a limited right of parents to opt out of vaccinating their children for medical reasons. Many also permit religious or philosophical exemptions. However, just because parents have a right to opt out, that does not necessarily mean that pediatricians have a legal or ethical obligation to continue to offer services to their children.

The case of Ricky is different from many other conflicts in pediatrics, because Dr. Wilson's concern is not only for Ricky's welfare, but also for that of her other patients. As noted in the scenario, many of these patients may not yet be candidates for vaccination as a consequence of immature age or medical factors. In addition, some vaccines are simply not effective in some patients, so the only true protection is to keep these patients away from others who are at risk. If enough people are vaccinated, even those in whom the vaccine does not work will be protected, because the likelihood of them coming into contact with someone else who is either not vaccinated or in whom the vaccine did not "take" is extremely low. This epidemiological principle is known as "herd immunity."

While the threat of autism from the measles vaccine has been widely rejected by the scientific community, and is based upon a fraudulent study conducted by former physician Andrew Wakefield, no vaccine is without some minimal risks. However, the collective benefits of every child being vaccinated—namely, the eradication of measles cases—vastly outweighs those risks. Roger and Adeline are correct to state the odds of contracting measles are generally low; however, they are low because most children have been vaccinated. If more families opted out, the risk would rise. This is a "collective action problem," sometimes called the "dilemma of the commons." One might say that, by taking advantage of the low risk resulting from the widespread vaccination of others, Adeline and Roger are freeloading.

Physicians outside the hospital and emergency setting can generally choose their patients with very few restrictions. As long as Dr. Wilson gives Adeline and Roger a reasonable amount of time to find another provider for Ricky, she is well within her legal rights to turn them away. Whether it is ethical for her to disrupt their therapeutic relationship in this coercive manner is a far more challenging question.

47

The Evidence Is in His Leg

DURING A ROBBERY, a shopkeeper, Silas, is shot by an armed assailant. After he is wounded, Silas returns fire and hits the attacker in the thigh. The shopkeeper dies before he can describe the perpetrator to the police, mumbling only, "I shot him in the leg. I shot him in the leg."

The police suspect a known criminal named Wesley, who showed up in the emergency room of a city hospital two hours after the robbery with a bullet wound in his leg. The police would like to compare that bullet to the rounds remaining in Silas's handgun. However, when Wesley realizes that the bullet may be used as evidence against him, he refuses to consent to surgery to remove it. The doctors believe that without the bullet removed, Wesley may suffer from some chronic pain and possibly a limp, but with proper wound care, he is unlikely to die or experience other long-term consequences. No other direct evidence ties Wesley to the crime other than the bullet wound.

Should police be able to have doctors remove the bullet from his leg—a relatively safe operation that can be conducted under local anesthesia—in order to present it as evidence at his trial?

———

REFLECTION: Searches and Seizures

THE ISSUE OF the surgical removal of potential evidence arises infrequently but has been the subject of a surprising amount of legal and ethical scholarship. The Fourth Amendment to the US Constitution forbids unreasonable searches and seizures, while the canons of medical ethics generally prohibit involuntary infringements of bodily integrity, at least when performed upon competent patients. Yet the prosecution of alleged criminals is a vital state interest that protects the public, so both physicians and judges have struggled to find the right balance.

In the 1970s, attorney John Cain advanced an argument for distinguishing between major and minor surgeries; under Cain's criteria, major surgery to retrieve evidence was never to be permitted, but minor surgery might be permitted under compelling circumstances. In the Supreme Court case of Winston v. Lee (1985), Justice William Brennan adopted a "reasonableness" standard that incorporated both the seriousness of the operation and the importance of the evidence. Rather than a blanket rule, Brennan believed these matters ought to be decided on a case-by-case basis. In the particular case of Rudolph Lee Jr., an alleged robber who refused to have a bullet extracted from beneath his collarbone, Brennan noted that the state had "substantial additional evidence" available that made the argument for forced surgery unconvincing.

A factor complicating the involuntary extraction of evidence is the role of physicians. It is one matter for the state to assert a right to retrieve evidence surgically but quite another for them to commandeer doctors into the process of retrieving it—especially if those physicians are unwilling. This issue has arisen most frequently with regard to the forcible drawing of blood during traffic stops. Two states, Hawaii and Idaho, now require medical personnel to engage in phlebotomy, even over a patient's objections, when instructed to do so by law enforcement. Only South Dakota law overtly shields physicians who refuse. With surgical procedures, prosecutors largely rely on the willingness of surgeons to perform involuntary evidence extractions. If no surgeons were willing to engage in such procedures, courts would likely prove reluctant to order them to do so.

Some ethicists maintain that any surgical intervention to retrieve evidence, conducted against a patient's will, is always unethical. For them, removing the bullet from Wesley's leg is inherently unacceptable. In contrast, for ethicists who accept Justice Brennan's balancing approach, the case for performing forced surgery upon Wesley appears reasonably strong: the surgery is minor and the alleged crime serious, while the bullet appears to be the decisive piece of evidence.

48

Echoes of Tuskegee

TREATMENT FOR A bone infection, or osteomyelitis, usually requires four to six weeks of intravenous antibiotics. Researchers at a university in the United States would like to test whether a shorter course of antibiotics, lasting only two weeks, can prove effective in most cases. However, setting up a study that compares patients receiving two weeks and those receiving four weeks of antibiotics would never be approved in the US, because the four- to six-week treatment regimen is known to be highly effective.

Instead, the researchers want to conduct their study in a developing nation in sub-Saharan Africa, where they have a positive relationship with public health authorities. In that nation, most patients who contract osteomyelitis go untreated, and many die. The researchers plan to offer a group of such patients, who would otherwise receive no treatment, a two-week course of antibiotics to see if it is effective. They will provide other basic medical care as well, but will not offer anyone the longer course of antibiotics that is already known to work.

Is this research ethical in the African nation even though it would not be permitted in the United States?

~~~

REFLECTION: Research Standards

MEDICAL RESEARCH IN the US has a checkered record of experimenting on vulnerable populations. Much of the lay public now knows of the Tuskegee syphilis experiment (1932–1972), during which government researchers observed the natural course of syphilis in a cohort of impoverished African American men while denying treatment to them. Other well-known troubling studies have also been conducted in the US—on developmentally impaired children at the Willowbrook State School in New York, to investigate hepatitis, and on prisoners at Stateville Penitentiary in Illinois, to learn more about malaria. Historian Harriet Washington reviews much of the chilling history of research on African Americans in the book Medical Apartheid (2007). Such experiments led to a public outcry and eventually to passage of the National Research Act (1974) and the creation of the National Commission for the Protection of Human Subjects of Biomedical and Behavioral Research. The Belmont Report of 1979 and the US Department of Health and Human Services' Common Rule of 1981 resulted in the establishment of institutional review boards (IRBs) designed to prevent such abuses in the future.

During the HIV/AIDS epidemic of the 1980s and 1990s, researchers found their sincere efforts to create cheaper and more effective drugs were hampered by IRB rules. Some turned abroad, to nations like Uganda and Thailand, to conduct studies that could not have been conducted in the United States.

Many of these protocols were designed to expand knowledge of existing interventions and lacked what is known as "clinical equipoise," a genuine uncertainty as to whether one treatment is better than another. Others tested a novel treatment while withholding an existing treatment known to be effective.

The proposed osteomyelitis study, for instance, does the latter. Advocates for this kind of research argue that the subjects, while not receiving treatment that meets the standard of care in developed nations, nonetheless end up no worse off—and usually better off—than they would be without participating. Some subjects do receive a treatment that may work. All receive general medical care. Without the experiment, none of the subjects would likely receive either of these benefits. Of course, one might logically conduct the experiments in impoverished or isolated communities within the United States on the same grounds—except that no IRB would ever approve such an arrangement.

Health ministers in several nations have welcomed Western scientists to set up such studies, hoping the results would improve healthcare access. In contrast, Marcia Angell, the former editor of the New England Journal of Medicine, has proved among the fiercest critics of such a two-tiered system of research norms. To Angell, Western doctors are ethically obligated to uphold the same standards elsewhere in the world as they do in the United States.

A closely related challenge is what is to be done with data that science later concludes was obtained through unethical experimentation. At the extreme are the results of medical experiments conducted at Nazi concentration camps. Harvard surgeon Robert Berger identified thirty such projects, the best-known of which were the immersion-hypothermia experiments conducted under Nazi doctor Sigmund Rascher at Dachau. An increasing consensus exists that the data from these experiments is not of scientific value, a position advanced by Berger and Arnold Relman, another former editor in chief of the New England Journal of Medicine, but the studies have nonetheless been cited in several dozen journal articles. As late as the 1980s, hypothermia expert Robert Pozos offered a spirited defense of their potential value. Whatever the particular worth of Nazi data, one might ask who "owns" the legacy of this research: Should the few individual survivors of these ghastly experiments or those groups who speak for victims of the Holocaust more generally have any say in determining the use of the data?

In a New England Journal commentary in 1990, Angell staked out an absolutist position against using data from experiments in the developing world that could not be conducted ethically in the United States. Angell observed that opponents of the "use of such data believe that it would tend to blunt the horror of what happened and thus in a sense dishonor those who died and offend the sensibilities of those who survived." Yet her primary objections were more forward-looking: namely, that publishing unethical data of any sort would encourage other scientists to continue to act unethically. Since publication is the currency of academic science, the hope was that removing the principal incentive for misconduct might reduce such malfeasance. Angell's opinion proved highly influential; many other editors have followed her lead. Whether ethical or not, the researchers in the osteomyelitis scenario might have trouble finding a major journal willing to accept their resulting article for publication.

49

"It Will Help Others, Not You"

Dr. Crusher, a pediatric oncologist, believes that a specific form of pediatric brain tumor is closely associated with early childhood exposure to certain chemicals. To test her theory, she wants to conduct a study that will take biopsies of these always-fatal tumors from afflicted children and compare them with the chemical-exposure histories reported by the children's parents. She hopes that the biopsy samples of those children exposed to the chemicals will display distinctive neurochemical markers, while those children who also have tumors but whose parents report no chemical exposure will not have these markers. In the long run, her goal is to demonstrate a chemical exposure–brain tumor connection that will lead to restrictions on these chemicals, ultimately saving children's lives.

The catch to this study is that the children involved will not benefit directly in any way. In fact, they will have to undergo a brain biopsy, which comes with risks: infection, bleeding, pain at the extraction site. Since these children are too young to consent on their own—most are between three and five years old—Dr. Crusher plans to seek permission from their parents.

She intends to persuade them to participate by saying, in part, "Think of all the other parents and children you'll be helping." Should this study be permitted?

—∽∾∽—

REFLECTION: Research or Treatment?

ONE OF THE fundamental differences between research studies and clinical medicine is that investigative subjects should not expect to benefit from their participation in studies. In fact, subjects in scientific research, such as pharmaceutical trials, may actually be harmed. For instance, drugmaker Eli Lilly halted late-stage trials of its promising Alzheimer's disease treatment, semagacestat, in 2010, after participants showed increased cognitive decline and higher rates of skin cancer. All six participants in a 2006 trial of the synthetic antibody TGN1412 became critically ill. Yet despite highly publicized negative outcomes, such as the death of eighteen-year-old Jesse Gelsinger in a University of Pennsylvania gene therapy study in 1999, many participants mistakenly believe they will benefit from participating in research. The mistaken belief, first described by psychiatric ethicist Paul Appelbaum, is called the "therapeutic misconception."

Medical sociologist Gail Henderson and her colleagues have defined the therapeutic misconception as occurring when "individuals do not understand that the defining purpose of clinical research is to produce generalizable knowledge, regardless of whether the subjects enrolled in the trial may potentially benefit from the intervention under study or from other aspects of the clinical trial." Patients in research studies—for one of many reasons—lose sight of the fact that they might not benefit. To many laypeople, research and healthcare appear very similar—both involve medical professionals, frequently dressed in white lab coats, providing interventions such as pharmaceuticals. Often these participants are desperate for help, having exhausted all known remedies.

Power imbalances between scientific experts, who are usually physicians, and patients, further complicate matters. Many research subjects, receiving experimental pills from doctors, simply trust these doctors (mistakenly) not to expose them to risk. In the pediatric setting, parents of subjects are vulnerable to the same misunderstandings and false optimism. One must ask to what degree the parents of potential participants in Dr. Crusher's proposed study truly understand that their own children will not benefit.

The federal government has designated children among the vulnerable populations—which also include pregnant women, cognitively impaired people, and prisoners—who deserve special protections as the subjects of research. In Dr. Crusher's scenario, these children will face genuine risks of medical complications at no benefit to themselves, and they are generally too young to assent meaningfully to such risks. Under these circumstances, the federal government allows institutional review boards (IRBs) to approve such studies only under narrow circumstances, including when risk is low and whether the study is of vital importance "for the understanding or amelioration of the subject's disorder or condition." (If the research does not meet these requirements, the US Department of Health and Human Services may, under certain circumstances, commission a panel of experts to authorize the study.) In practice, Dr. Crusher will have to convince an IRB that the increased risks of brain biopsics are minor to these patients and that the data she gathers will prove crucial in cancer research. IRBs can be notoriously unsympathetic audiences, however, so she may have her work cut out for her.

50

Lithium in the Water

SEVERAL STRONG EPIDEMIOLOGICAL studies have demonstrated that regions of the world where the element lithium occurs naturally in the drinking water have lower suicide rates. (The current proposed theory is that lithium is a protective factor in brain development, so it may take decades for the benefits of such lithium exposure to pay off in suicide prevention.) No known negative side effects have been associated with trace lithium exposure, but few long-term studies have been conducted to detect such risks.

The epidemiological studies on lithium have drawn the attention of Otis, the mayor of small English city that has one of the highest suicide rates in the Western world. Otis proposes adding trace amounts of lithium to the drinking water in his community to see if this intervention will help. He believes this might, in the long run, prevent up to fifty unnecessary deaths each year. "If you don't want to be exposed to lithium," says Otis, "you can always buy bottled water."

Is Otis's proposal ethical?

REFLECTION: Preventing Suicide

THE DATA SUPPORTING a link between lithium in the drinking water and lower rates of suicide is surprisingly robust. Studies in Texas, Japan, Austria, and Greece have all demonstrated similar findings; the Texas study showed a decrease in violent crimes such as homicide and rape as well. (One must emphasize that these are not the levels of lithium used to treat mental illness but trace amounts measured in micrograms per liter.) An analogy might be drawn to the trace amounts of fluoride added to drinking water to prevent tooth decay, which the Centers for Disease Control describes as one of the ten greatest public health achievements of the twentieth century, but which continues to be opposed by alternative medicine advocates, libertarians, Christian Scientists, and others on the political right and left. Assuming that lithium prevents suicide, this does not necessarily mean it should be added to the water supply. Rather, such a decisions must be weighed against the costs of doing so, including economic expense, the rights of those opposed to lithium exposure, and concern for theoretical long-term side effects of such exposure. For all we know—and there is no data for this, but it is always possible—people in the lithium-exposed communities that have lower suicide rates are also less creative or courageous.

One risk of opposing the addition of lithium is falling for what is often called an "appeal to nature"—the belief that something is better or healthier because it is naturally occurring. (This concept ought not to be confused with the "naturalistic fallacy," an unrelated concept proposed by British philosopher G. E. Moore.) Many substances that occur naturally, such as arsenic, are quite toxic; others that are synthetic, such as aspirin, can be highly therapeutic. Lithium occurs naturally in the drinking water in some regions and not in others, but that tells us little about whether it is ethical to add it to the drinking water where it is not present. Presumably there is not a significant difference, morally speaking, between diverting lithium-rich water to a lithium-poor watershed and merely adding the lithium to the water in the latter area. Both achieve identical outcomes, albeit one in an arguably less natural manner.

When evaluating any uses of publicly shared resources like the water supply, one should not ask whether the use is natural, but rather whether it is health-promoting or serves the public. Forming consensus on such a subject is not easy, however, as the conflict over fluoridation demonstrates. Until the public can better understand the illogic of appeals to nature, proposals like Otis's are unlikely to gain much political traction.

51

"Why Didn't You Warn Me I Was At Risk?'

SEVERAL FORMS OF colon cancer are inherited and affect patients at an early age. The offspring of these patients are advised to undergo frequent colonoscopies to detect precancerous growths that can either be excised individually or that require removal of the entire colon. This has been known to oncologists since the 1950s.

In 1995, Moe was diagnosed with early-onset colon cancer. Patients with Moe's specific variant of inherited cancer generally develop the disease between ages forty and seventy; Moe was forty-two. Moe instructed his oncologist, Dr. Jekyll, that under no condition did he want his family to learn that he had cancer. "It's my business," he says. "Why make them worry when this might not affect them until they're seventy years old?" Moe's children grow up believing that their father died of an untreated intestinal blockage.

Twenty years after Moe's death, his eldest daughter, Maureen, develops colon cancer at the age of forty-one. Her oncologist informs her of the genetic nature of her condition, which leads her to investigate more closely her father's medical history. In a box of his papers, she discovers the medical records from his treatment by Dr. Jekyll. These include the diagnosis of early-onset colon cancer. Maureen immediately hires a lawyer and sues Dr. Jekyll, who is still in practice, for negligence. In her state, the statute of limitations did not start to run until she discovered her injury, so it is still possible for her to make a claim.

Should Dr. Jekyll be liable for damages?

REFLECTION: Inherited Diseases and Privacy

THE LEGAL AND ethical duties of physicians to individuals who are not their patients have expanded significantly over the past half century. Whereas once claims of doctor-patient confidentiality absolved providers of most obligations toward third parties, courts have now trimmed those protections substantially. Many state laws, modeled on California's "Tarasoff rule," require psychiatrists to warn and/or protect the potential victims of dangerous patients. Some states expect physicians treating patients suffering from contagious diseases to notify family members of their risk. In the Tennessee case of Bradshaw v. Daniel (1993), a court for the first time expanded that duty to warn relatives of noncontagious patients as well. In that case, the wife of a man treated for Rocky Mountain spotted fever was not informed that she might have been exposed to the illness through the same source as had her husband. She later also died of the disease, and her family won a lawsuit on the grounds that she had not been advised to seek medical care. In addition, several jurisdictions have enacted mandatory partner-notification statutes, requiring physicians to report patients testing positive for the AIDS-causing HIV virus to the health authorities, who will then inform the patients' at-risk contacts of their exposure. The widespread rise of genetic diagnoses and testing has raised the question of what duties physicians may owe to patients' family members at future risk of hereditary disease.

The first two courts to address the question of whether the risk of genetic illness should be shared with a patient's relatives decided the matter differently. In Pate v. Threlkel (1995), the Florida Supreme Court, noting the importance of physician-patient confidentiality, ruled that a physician had fulfilled his duties when he told the patient herself of her family's risk; it was therefore the moral obligation of the patient, not the doctor, to pass this information along to vulnerable relatives. A year later, in Safer v. Estate of Pack, the New Jersey courts arrived at precisely the opposite conclusion, finding negligence where a physician failed to warn the patient's child directly of her genetic risk of colon cancer. While telling patients of the danger to their relatives is now widely understood to be a part of sound medical practice, how to act when patients wish to keep the information secret remains controversial.

Both the American Society of Human Genetics (ASHG) and the President's Commission for the Study of Ethical Problems in Medicine and Biomedical and Behavioral Research issued specific guidelines on disclosing hereditary risks to family members. According to ASGH policy, such disclosure must meet the following four criteria: (1) efforts to get the patient to tell his family directly have failed; (2) the risk of serious harm is high; (3) a specific at-risk relative can be identified; and (4) methods of prevention or treatment exist, or early monitoring reduces risk. These guidelines conflict with those of the American Medical Association, whose principles favor maintaining confidentiality.

Unlike Dr. Jekyll, who cannot undo the damage to Maureen, future physicians may choose to inform patients in advance that they will breach genetic confidentiality, as a matter of policy, to protect relatives at risk. Such "fair warning" might, of course, drive some patients away from effective medical care. Most, however, will likely accept this as a necessary corollary of treatment. That approach would eliminate the need for litigation like Maureen's in the future, although it will offer little guidance to the judge in Dr. Jekyll's case.

52

The Boundaries between Mice and Men

A NEUROLOGY RESEARCHER has a novel idea for studying the mechanisms of diseases that affect brain cells, such as Parkinson's disease and Alzheimer's disease. She intends to inject human brain cells into mice embryos to trace their development. She estimates that the brains of these embryos would be 50 percent human and 50 percent mouse. The hybrid mice would be killed painlessly long before birth. The researcher would then study their hybrid brains for rudimentary elements of human cognition. Her long-term goal is to create mouse models for the development of drugs that can treat serious human diseases.

Should the researcher be allowed to go ahead with this experiment?

REFLECTION: Human-Animal Hybrids

UNTIL THE 1970s, animal chimeras—cross-species hybrids— were largely the stuff of mythology. Yet starting with the success of biologists Paul Berg and Richard Mulligan at Stanford University in transplanting rabbit hemoglobin genes into primate kidneys, scientists managed to generate a slew of rapid advances in the field: A hematologist at the University of Nevada, Reno, claimed to have produced sheep with livers that were partially "humanized"; a lab at the Mayo Clinic produced "pigs with human blood." In China, researchers fused human skin cells with rabbit eggs. Yet the most significant and controversial step in the field occurred when Irving Weissman, a professor in the departments of pathology and developmental biology at Stanford, asked for—and received—permission from the university to create mice embryos with brains derived from human neurons. Weissman had previously produced mice embryos whose neural tissue was 1 percent human, but he hoped that using only human neurons, coupled with mouse glial cells, would generate a model for studying human neural tissue in the laboratory.

Opponents of human-animal chimera research are particularly concerned about the use of neural tissue in these experiments. Critics fear that mice with human brain cells could develop some human cognitive qualities and could even experience humanlike suffering. These bioethicists often see the hybrids as an affront to human dignity. They also express concerns related to species integrity and human uniqueness—or what columnist Wesley J. Smith refers to as "human exceptionalism." Making mice more human, according to some commentators, also makes humans more like mice. Senator Sam Brownback of Kansas has introduced legislation multiple times to prohibit human-animal hybrids in research, but the bills have failed to gain traction.

Even ethicists who favor such research in principle have urged considerable caution on the part of researchers. Legal scholar Henry Greely and his colleagues, in an article in the prestigious American Journal of Bioethics, noted that these experiments would be problematic, even if not inherently unethical, if they so unsettled the public that they "undermined support for . . . other useful biomedical research." However, any initial popular concern over Weissman's request has largely evaporated, and human-mouse hybrids are increasingly part of scientific endeavors. The most striking feature of the scenario at the start of this chapter may be that at many universities today, the prospect of mice with half-human brains is neither surprising nor particularly controversial among researchers—although the idea of such chimeras still remains highly objectionable to a large segment of the US public.

53

Doctoring a Dictator

FOZZIE IS THE brutal dictator of a wealthy nation that enjoys a long-standing military alliance with the United States. He develops a rare leukemia, a blood cancer, which is resistant to conventional chemotherapies. However, there is a drug trial about to begin at a major US hospital for a promising but experimental new therapeutic agent that may treat this variant of the disease. Fozzie secures an emergency visa and arranges with the hospital to participate in the study, which holds out the only realistic chance of saving his life.

Dr. Steven Strange, the chief of oncology at the hospital, had initially agreed to allow Fozzie to receive the experimental treatment. Yet on the same day Fozzie arrives, before the treatment begins, Dr. Strange's friend gives him a book on human rights abuses in Fozzie's nation. Dr. Strange reads enough of the book to learn that Fozzie's government is responsible for the deaths of thousands of innocent civilians and has been implicated in sexual violence, torture, and even cannibalism. He is troubled by the prospect offering a treatment that will allow Fozzie to continue to rule when Fozzie's people have no access to basic medical care or the most fundamental human rights. "Lots of people die of leukemia in his country," says Dr. Strange's friend. "None of them are allowed to come to the United States for experimental treatments."

Is it ethical for Dr. Strange to refuse to provide the experimental treatment to Fozzie?

REFLECTION: Human Rights and Treatment

THE LEADERS OF developing nations, both dictators and those democratically elected, have a long history of traveling to wealthy Western countries for medical care. The result is that the world's leading democracies often play medical host to the planet's most brutal rulers. In 2012, Ethiopian strongman Meles Zenawi died while undergoing treatment in Belgium. That same year, Saudi Crown Prince Nayef received cancer treatments in Cleveland and later died in Geneva, Switzerland. Spain played host to dying Gabonese dictator Omar Bongo in 2009 and Angolan strongman José Eduardo dos Santos in 2017, while Germany has welcomed Kazakh despot Nursultan Nazarbayev for regular medical checkups. Professor Ian Taylor, an expert on African politics, has noted that of the ten African heads of state to die of natural causes between 2000 and 2015, all received foreign medical care and eight died abroad. Many of these nations have deplorable human rights records, and their populations have highly limited access to healthcare of any meaningful quality. Yet possibly the most famous case occurred when President Jimmy Carter allowed the former shah of Iran to undergo surgery at New York Hospital in Manhattan in 1979. Carter's decision, widely criticized at home and internationally, led to a major foreign policy crisis. .

Surprisingly, the bioethics community has remained relatively silent on this subject. As a general principle, medical ethics favors that healthcare be delivered apolitically. When Bahrain placed medical professionals, such as nurse Rula al-Saffar, on trial for providing emergency first aid to antigovernment protesters in 2011, numerous international medical associations condemned the government's actions. Similarly, physicians' groups have criticized the targeting of doctors by all sides in the Syrian Civil War. However, such efforts to keep medicine apolitical make it difficult for these same organizations to raise their voices when dictators seek treatment abroad. Although a few commentators have suggested rules requiring world leaders to receive healthcare in their own nations, these efforts remain quixotic.

Just because the US government has given Fozzie a visa, however, does not mean that Dr. Strange has an ethical obligation to treat him. In fact, physicians generally have no obligation to treat anyone with whom they do not already have an established relationship. (One might argue that such a relationship was created when Dr. Strange initially agreed to enroll Fozzie into the protocol, but as treatment has not yet started, this is debatable.) Patients are turned away from potentially life-saving experimental therapies all the time—often as a result of circumstances beyond their control, such as that a study reaches its enrollment limited. Unlike Fozzie, these individuals often die without ever even learning that such studies are ongoing.

Dr. Strange may wish to take into account the broader impact of rejecting Fozzie as a patient. The result may be the further politicization of medicine and could make it more difficult for groups such as the World Health Organization and the International Council of Nurses to protest the treatment of physicians abroad. Or the refusal may serve as a statement that draws public attention to the plight of the victims of human rights abuses under Fozzie's dictatorship. Yet physicians are often constrained in any efforts to publicize their refusals: dictators generally want their medical treatment kept secret, and confidentiality laws prevent doctors from publicizing such requests without permission. The truth is that the public has very little idea of how many problematic leaders seek medical care in their countries. Doctors may be refusing to provide care to such autocrats all of the time. There is no way of knowing. Yet just because the public is unlikely to learn of Dr. Strange's decision does not absolve him of the choice of whether to treat her controversial patient.

PART FIVE

Practical Matters

M edical ethics is often framed as a question of what *should* be done. In the context of the modern healthcare system, it also reflects an assessment of what *can* be done. Once governed by informal professional norms, healthcare is now regulated by complex federal and state regulations, including the Health Insurance Portability and Accountability Act (HIPAA) of 1996 and the Affordable Care Act (ACA) of 2010. These rules are frequently in flux; uncertainty remains, for example, whether Congress will repeal portions of the ACA (a.k.a. Obamacare) in the near future.

Doctors were once answerable primarily to their patients and their colleagues. Now they find themselves navigating tangled webs of agency regulations, hospital bylaws, and insurance bureaucracies. How to serve the interests of their patients, in the context of a system that often renders such service challenging, is one of the significant burdens of contemporary medicine. As medicine becomes more of a business and less of a "learned calling," many doctors must grapple with issues related to cost containment and resource scarcity. The challenges that arise around the business of medicine have become the bread and butter of many healthcare policy gurus, as well as the bane of many a hospital-based bioethicist.

54

Screening Future Employees

A LARGE-SCALE STUDY has shown that people who have certain genetic markers on chromosome 15 and also smoke cigarettes are far more likely to develop lung cancer than those who do not carry such markers. This study comes to the attention of Irwin, the owner of the Happy & Healthy Tobacco Company, which manufactures cigarettes. Irwin is concerned that his employees, many of whom smoke tobacco, will develop lung cancer—which would be bad for both his company's health-care costs and its public image. He decides to require all future employees to be tested for these genetic markers, and plans to hire only those who test negative.

Should our society permit him to require this sort of genetic testing of prospective employees?

———

REFLECTION: Genetic Discrimination

CONGRESS PASSED THE Genetic Information Nondiscrimination Act of 2008 (GINA) with bipartisan backing. Both President Bill Clinton and President George W. Bush had advocated for the bill; it passed the Senate 95–0 and the House of Representatives 414–1, with only Libertarian congressman Ron Paul dissenting. The legislation bans discrimination in employment and health insurance on the basis of one's genetics. (Notably, however, life insurance and disability insurance are not covered, leaving an ongoing deterrent to genetic testing.) The purpose of the law was to combat "genoism," a term coined by *Gattaca* film director Andrew Niccol to describe discrimination against a person based on his genetic résumé. While employers can test for a condition likely to cause current harm, they cannot test for future risks. So a bus company would be allowed to test drivers for a gene mutation likely to cause sudden heart attacks or seizures on the job at present, but not a mutation expected to cause blindness down the road.

Advocates of the law compare genetic discrimination to racial prejudice. Critics are quick to slam this analogy. Columnist Andrew Sullivan wrote in the *New York Times*: "The point of laws against racial bias is to outlaw *irrational* discrimination based on irrelevant characteristics. The point of laws against genetic discrimination is to outlaw *rational* bias based on relevant information." [Italics added.] While Sullivan conceded that such genetic data is "speculative," he argued that it was speculative in the same way that SAT scores are speculative: some low performers may succeed in college, but that does not mean the tests do not have some predictive value. Similarly, then, Irwin's plan to hire only employees who test negative for lung cancer markers on chromosome 15 could be considered perfectly rational, whether or not it is just.

Allowing discrimination based upon genetic risks that may display themselves in the future strikes many people as unfair, but is it really so much more unfair than discriminating against traits that already display themselves? Nobody would expect Greyhound to hire a blind bus driver. So why expect it to hire a bus driver who has a genetic condition that makes her 99 percent likely to go blind within five years? The company would squander resources training an employee who would not able to work in the near future, while that employee would lose an opportunity to learn a trade she could continue to perform after her blindness sets in.

More concern exists, however, for prospective employees who have conditions likely to prevent employment anywhere. One can easily imagine a situation where companies outside the tobacco industry also refuse to hire workers positive for the lung cancer markers on chromosome 15. The law offers blanket protections against employment discrimination for such genetically unlucky individuals. How to permit rational genetic discrimination without closing off meaningful opportunities for those who have lost the so-called genetic lottery remains an unresolved ethical dilemma.

55

"I Want a White Surgeon"

A PATIENT, HECTOR, is admitted to the hospital for an emergency appendectomy. Without surgery, he runs a high risk of a burst appendix and death. The patient, who is a well-known activist in the white supremacy movement, will agree to the surgery on the condition that only Caucasian surgeons operate on him. Hector says that nonwhite hospital staff, such as nursing assistants, may be present in the room, but they may not touch his body. If the hospital cannot accommodate his request, he states that he would rather die than violate his convictions.

Should the hospital provide him with an all-white surgical team, and if not, should they operate against his wishes or allow him to die?

REFLECTION: Patient Prejudice

REQUESTS RELATED TO the identity of the caregiver generally occur along a continuum. Some requests, like those of a Ku Klux Klan member demanding a white doctor, strike much of society as disturbing, if not repugnant. Others, such as a pregnant teenage girl requesting a female gynecologist for her first obstetric exam, appear much more reasonable to many people. Numerous cases stand in a gray area between these extremes— for example, the African American psychiatric patient who requests that an African American psychiatrist evaluate him, because he fears that a white doctor can't understand what he has experienced. Practical exigencies and consequences may also come into play: a patient whose request for a home health aide of a specific ethnicity or gender is rejected may find pre-texts for firing aides who do not meet her requirements until her specifications are met.

While data regarding racial attitudes of patients is not available, research shows that a sizable number of patients have personal preferences for the gender of their physicians. For instance, one 2005 study showed that pediatric patients pre-ferred female providers while their parents preferred male providers. By contrast, a 2016 investigation found that only 1 in 10 adults cared about the gender of their doctor—although that percentage, at the population level, is still a large absolute num-ber of patients. (Complicating the subject even further, a study published in *JAMA Internal Medicine* in 2017 found that certain elderly patients actually achieve better outcomes when treated by female providers.) Religious beliefs further complicate mat-ters. Reasonable people might sympathize with the request of an Orthodox rabbi who asks for a male urologist for his pros-tatectomy because his religion objects to an unrelated woman touching him, if such contact can be avoided. Far fewer people sympathize with a male patient who demands a male urologist under the mistaken belief that "women are too emotional to cut straight."

Hospitals and courts would prefer to avoid the time and energy involved in investigating the motivations of those who make such race- and gender-specific requests, but in the case of Hector, the hospital has three distinct options. It can honor Hector's request regarding his care providers' race and arrange for an all-white surgical team. It can defy Hector's request and, declaring this a medical emergency, forcibly treat him with a multiracial surgical team. Or it can refuse to honor Hector's request for a white surgical team but honor his related request regarding his right to die if the only other option is a non-white surgeon. Few patients are likely to hold beliefs as strong as Hector's on race, so accommodating such rare requests is unlikely to cause significant disruptions in the overall delivery of healthcare. Letting Hector die because he holds views that many find objectionable might strike many physicians as out of keeping with the nobler traditions of medicine. At the same time, honoring such requests runs the risk of stamping members of certain ethnic, racial, or gender groups with a "badge of inferiority," leading to demoralization. This effect might be particularly concerning if the same groups of providers were consistently excluded, resulting in increased social acceptance of such prejudices.

56

"We Don't Tell Our Elders They Have Cancer"

AGATHA IS A ninety-year-old woman who arrives at the hospital coughing up blood and is rapidly diagnosed with a terminal lung tumor. Before the physician on duty, Dr. Zhivago, can inform Agatha of her diagnosis, her daughter, Delia, arrives at the hospital and requests to speak with Zhivago. She tells him that her mother grew up in a small isolated nation in the Caucasus and immigrated to the United States only in her seventies, following the collapse of the Soviet Union. "In our culture," explains Delia, we don't tell our elders they have cancer. We certainly don't tell them that they are going to die. Please tell her she has an infection, but that it is nothing to worry about. Trust me, she would not want to know the truth."

Delia's brother, Victor, arrives several minutes later and also urges Dr. Zhivago not to inform his mother of her terminal cancer diagnosis. He says: "Mama thinks like the people she grew up around, not like an American. No doctor in her homeland would ever dream of telling a patient she is going to die. What right do you have to take away our mother's hope?

Besides, what's the point of upsetting her when there is nothing to be done?"

Should Dr. Zhivago withhold the diagnosis and prognosis from this elderly patient?

REFLECTION: Autonomy and Culture

ONE OF THE fundamental principles of modern medicine in the US is that patients should have the autonomy to make their own healthcare decisions. One might think of this as the Frank Sinatra rule: "I'll do it my way." For patients to make informed decisions, physicians need to apprise them of their diagnoses and treatment options. It is worth noting that this has not always been the case: in 1961, a well-known survey conducted by physician Donald Oken revealed that 90 percent of doctors would *not* reveal a terminal cancer diagnosis to a patient. Withholding such information remains standard practice in some non-Western nations. The question arises whether Agatha should be treated as other American patients, or in line with the cultural norms of her birthplace. Doctors will want to conform to her wishes, of course, but it may prove difficult to discern what her wishes would be without compromising them. Dr. Zhivago could ask: "Would you want me to tell you if you were dying of cancer?" Unfortunately, that is not far removed from asking one's spouse, "Would you want me to inform you that I'm cheating on you?" Sharing the question would also reveal the probable answer.

What one might do in Agatha's case is inquire, as part of a series of general questions about medicine and familial health, "Has anybody in your family ever died of cancer?" Most patients, based on statistical averages, will say yes. The physician might then ask, "How did you or your family handle the situation? Did you tell him?" If the patient were to respond, "Of course not. Are you crazy, doctor? Why would we do something like that?" then one has a strong indication of how the patient would wish her own case to be handled. Similarly, if the patient were to say, "Of course we did," that would also help guide care. However, these techniques will not establish clarity in all circumstances.

One approach to these cases suggests weight should be placed on whether treatment decisions must yet be made. If there is truly nothing to be done, then a stronger argument exists for erring on the side of withholding information. However, if decisions still need to be rendered—about palliative radiation, for instance—then one might lean toward revealing the diagnosis in situations in which the patient's preferences about knowing her diagnosis prove truly impossible to ascertain. The flaw in this approach is that *all* patients have end-of-life decisions to be made, although some choices do not relate to medical care. If Agatha were to find out that she is dying, she might wish to rewrite her will, or to return to her homeland for a final time, or take a luxury cruise. Denying medical autonomy can often result in denying nonmedical autonomy as well.

57

"The Best Treatment Is Prayer"

MINA, A SIXTY-FIVE-YEAR-OLD widow, falls on the sidewalk, is brought to the emergency room at a community hospital with a broken femur, and has her leg surgically repaired. On day three of her hospitalization, she develops bacterial pneumonia—which can usually be treated with antibiotics. Without treatment, many patients die. Mina refuses antibiotics. She says that she is a Christian Scientist and that the best treatment for her pneumonia is prayer. "Antibiotics won't work," she says. "In fact, using antibiotics will show God that I don't have absolute faith and will interfere with the efficacy of my prayers."

While the doctors are deciding how to handle this situation, Mina's daughter, Fiona, arrives at the hospital. She has traveled from out of state, coming as soon as she learned that her mother was ill. Fiona demands that the doctors treat her mother with antibiotics. "She only became a Christian Scientist last month when she started dating a new boyfriend," says Fiona. "For sixty-four years, she was a run-of-the-mill Methodist like the rest of our family." Mina confirms this story but insists she can convert to any religion she wants at any time for any reason.

Should the doctors try to get a court order to treat Mina over her vocal objections?

REFLECTION: Cognitive Capacity

BEFORE PATIENT ARE granted the autonomy to make their own medical decisions, they must meet certain basic cognitive standards, which are referred to as "having capacity." Multiple tests for capacity exist, but the best-known is one described by psychiatric ethicist Paul Appelbaum and psychologist Thomas Grisso in 1988 in a seminal article in the *New England Journal of Medicine*. Appelbaum and Grisso asked that patients communicate a consistent choice, understand information relevant to their medical condition, appreciate the consequences of various proposed interventions, and be able to manipulate information rationally.

Christian Scientists generally do not meet these standards. While they accept treatment for injury, they usually reject medication for illness because they believe that prayer may cure illness and modern pharmaceuticals will not. In short, they doubt the efficacy of medicine. (This contrasts with Jehovah's Witnesses, for example, who reject blood transfusions; Jehovah's Witnesses acknowledge the efficacy of such transfusions—i.e., "they work"—but view them as banned by the Bible.) While prayer may or may not help patients in distress, a question about which there is considerable disagreement, antibiotics *do* cure bacterial pneumonia. Although Christian Scientists refuse to accept these medical "truths," they are permitted to make their own medical decisions—an exception to Appelbaum and Grisso's principles. However, they may not make similar decisions for their children.

If Mina had been a Christian Scientist her entire life, the consensus among medical ethicists would be to allow her to refuse care under these circumstances. Complicating the situation is her recent conversion. Professor Edward N. Beiser of Brown University often described the challenge in such cases as "the Jell-O test." Almost all of us, as children, have watched our parents or grandparents make Jell-O: first, pouring colored powder into a pan of boiling water and then refrigerating it until it cools into Jell-O about an hour later. The more impatient among us likely opened the refrigerator halfway through the process, probably several times—trying to determine at which precise moment the colored water gelled into Jell-O. Similarly, bioethicists must ask how long, loud, and consistent a patient's change of heart must be before her new beliefs can govern her medical decisions. Is one month as a Christian Scientist long enough? Three days? Half an hour? As the stakes rise—and especially in matters of life and death—hospitals and physicians often ask for longer, stronger periods of consistency.

58

Well-Intentioned Fraud

A MIDDLE-AGED WOMAN, Vivien, appears for her first appointment with an oncologist, Dr. Bock, to begin treatment for a rare form of cancer. She is accompanied by her sister, Jeanne, to whom she bears a striking resemblance. On evaluation, the physician notes several major inconsistencies between the patient's medical records and the findings from her physical exam. Most notably, previous doctors have documented that the patient lost her left index finger in an automobile accident, but Vivien appears to have all ten of her digits intact.

Dr. Bock confronts Vivien about these inconsistencies, and she confesses that she is actually Jeanne and that the two sisters have conspired to exchange identities because Jeanne has health insurance while Vivien is an undocumented resident of the United States and has no way of obtaining insurance or paying for cancer treatments. The chemotherapy required to treat her cancer costs over $150,000, and the sisters cannot realistically raise that amount of money quickly. Vivien and Jeanne both plead with the doctor to "overlook" his discovery. Dr. Bock sincerely believes that the treatments will save the woman's life.

Is it ethical for Dr. Bock to pretend he has not discovered the sisters' deceit and to provide "Vivien" with lifesaving care?

REFLECTION: Health Insurance

HEALTHCARE FRAUD IS a serious problem in the United States. The *Wall Street Journal* estimated that fraud accounted for 10 percent of all Medicare spending in 2013, or $58 billion. The Department of Health and Human Services warned in 2016 that 12 percent of Medicaid expenditures (more than $139 billion) reflected "improper payments." The phenomenon is also rampant among the privately insured. This fraud is not a victimless crime. These costs are either passed along to the general public through increased insurance rates, decreased services, or, in the case of government programs, tax hikes. In Jeanne's case, the sisters are in essence stealing $150,000 from the taxpayers.

Yet ethical assessment often requires an understanding of context. One must ask: Why is Jeanne stealing this expensive treatment from her fellow human beings? Critics of the existing healthcare structure might well argue that she is doing so because society has created a system that is inherently unjust. A wealthy nation ought to be able to provide lifesaving chemotherapy at an affordable cost to a law-abiding middle-aged woman in desperate need. While some believe that spending almost 18 percent of our gross domestic product on healthcare may be too much, there is also a compelling argument that 18 percent is too little, if women like Jeanne must otherwise go without care. That additional expenditure would have to come from somewhere—whether military hardware or education or consumer goods—but most of us, a priori, would gladly trade a few consumer goods for affordable chemotherapy if we were to develop cancer. So a case can be made that Vivien and Jeanne are acting dishonestly in the context of an unjust system.

One of the most difficult decisions physicians confront regularly is to what degree to look the other way when patients engage in activities that are illegal but may enhance their health or improve their welfare. These situations might include patients who split their pills with relatives or those who import cheaper medications illegally from abroad for their personal use. Such cases might also include homeless people who feign illness to gain admission to the hospital, seeking clean beds and warm meals that they have been unable to obtain elsewhere.

Dr. Bock ought to encourage "Vivien" to investigate any honest means for obtaining her treatment affordably. He might also mention to the sisters that they are likely to get caught: if *he* could see through their deception so easily, other providers are likely to do the same—and many will have a zero-tolerance policy. If Dr. Bock does look the other way, at no profit to himself, he might argue that he is doing on a larger scale what many other providers do every day with far smaller deceptions—aiding individual patients at the expense of healthcare insurers in the context of an often-Kafkaesque medical system. Whether he *should* do so is a different matter entirely.

59

A Most Expensive Patient

EDITH IS A sixty-three-year-old retired schoolteacher who lives with her husband, Herbert, and two dogs in a small town. She has six children and eleven grandchildren. One day, she notices odd discolorations under her skin, so Herbert drives her to the nearest hospital emergency room. She is diagnosed with a rare bleeding disorder of unknown cause. Fortunately, there is a treatment that cures most people—a very expensive clotting factor that costs $75,000 a vial. Most patients require only one or two vials.

For an unexplained reason, the clotting factor treats Edith's condition but does not cure it. As a result, she requires four vials of the remedy daily—at a total cost more than $2 million per week. She can enjoy her time in the hospital, visiting with family and crocheting sweaters for her grandkids, but since the treatment is both perishable and infused continuously, she is unable to leave the medical ward.

Edith and Herbert cannot afford these charges out of pocket, and their insurance is capped at $1 million per year. After Edith accrues more than $3 million in outstanding bills over ten days, nearly exhausting the hospital's entire annual budget for charity care, hospital officials discuss ending her treatment.

Would it be ethical to do so, or must the hospital keep treating her at its own expense—effectively diverting charity care away from hundreds of other patients?

―∽―

REFLECTION: Visible and Invisible Victims

In 2014, 1 percent of the US population accounted for 22.7 percent of healthcare costs, while the top 5 percent of users consumed 50 percent of all care, according to the Agency for Healthcare Research and Quality. Some individuals require even more expensive treatment: a retired prison guard named Slim Watson, suffering from a blood disorder similar to Edith's, spent thirty-four days in a North Carolina hospital in 2000—at a cost of $5.2 million. How much to spend on any one patient is among the crucial issues at the center of the debate over healthcare rationing. Few patients like Edith or Slim Watson can afford a multimillion-dollar hospital bill, and insurers cap payouts to avoid these extreme claims, so either the taxpayers or private hospitals will end up covering the costs. This likely means less money available in the healthcare system for other patients. Former Oregon governor John Kitzhaber, an emergency room physician, has written of "visible" and "invisible" victims. If we cut off care to Edith, we must watch a visible victim suffer and die. That is highly unpalatable to most physicians and much of the public. Yet if we allow these vast sums to be expended on Edith's case, we will create invisible victims—the patients who do not receive preventive checkups or complimentary flu shots, for example, and perish as a result. They are out of sight, so they may trouble us less. That does not necessarily mean that we have not done them wrong.

Philosopher John Rawls suggested that these questions of distributive justice be decided by pretending to wear a so-called "veil of ignorance": we must imagine a hypothetical world, one in which we have no knowledge of our own position or status, and then create rules that are most just for all concerned. Many of us, possibly including Edith, would not design a healthcare system a priori that spends $2 million per week on a single patient at the expense of countless others. At the same time, Edith is a flesh-and-blood human being. Simply informing her that she must die because she costs too much seems anathema to many people at a visceral level.

Moreover, once we stop paying for care for Edith, there are many other patients whose care is expensive, even if it does not reach such newsworthy levels. Often organ transplants, for instance, are not "cost-effective," in the sense that the dollars spent on these patients, if expended elsewhere in the health-care system, might preserve more lives for a longer time. Yet few ethicists advocate for abandoning organ transplantation or adopting a perfectly efficient utilitarian model of healthcare delivery that strives to achieve the greatest good for the greater number with mathematical exactitude. For many observers, Edith's case reveals a gap between the most rational choice (distributing money to save the most lives) and what feels just (saving the life of the human being in front of them).

60

When Doctors Choose Who Lives

A STATE IS developing a contingency plan for how to allocate ventilators (artificial respiration machines) in case of a severe flu pandemic on par with the flu pandemic of 1918–1919, which killed more than five hundred thousand Americans. Since a future pandemic could last months, while individuals often require ventilator support for only a matter of days to weeks before they recover, one ventilator could save several or even dozens of lives. Yet it will never be cost-effective or realistically possible to stockpile enough machines for the entire population.

Across the state, there are already some patients on long-term ventilator support in hospitals and nursing homes, including quadriplegic victims of spinal cord and brain injuries who cannot breathe on their own. These individuals live their entire lives with artificial respiration; without such ventilator support, they will die.

In the case of a pandemic, is it ethical to remove these long-term patients from their ventilators in order to use the machines to save the lives of a significantly larger number of acutely ill flu patients?

REFLECTION: Ventilator Allocation

ONE OF THE first questions to ask in addressing this scenario is whether the same medical rules that apply under ordinary circumstances should apply during times of a genuine health-care crisis. Most organizations and committees that have addressed the issue of ventilator allocation in a flu pandemic have answered this inquiry in the negative. During the course of regular hospital care, ventilator access usually occurs on a "first come, first served" basis. Experts nearly uniformly reject this approach in the case of a future pandemic. (Iron lungs were allocated in a "first come, first served" manner during the polio epidemics of the mid-twentieth century, often with unsatisfactory results.) Rather, specific inclusionary and exclusionary criteria need to be developed for such catastrophic circumstances. The ethical debate is not over whether triage should occur—that seems to have been decided—but over specifically who should be excluded.

A strong consensus exists that rules for allocation should be developed in advance, rather than on an ad hoc basis in a time of emergency. So far, the boldest effort to tackle this question occurred in New York in 2007 and 2015. A joint enterprise of the New York State Task Force on Life and the Law and the New York State Department of Health, led by highly regarded psychiatrist Tia Powell—set specific guidelines for ventilator eligibility. Among the exclusion criteria originally proposed were cardiac arrest, metastatic malignancy with poor prognosis, severe burns, and end-stage organ failure, including kidney failure. The last category, which encompassed all patients on dialysis, drew a public backlash. Yet the most significant decision of the group was one that largely avoided widespread public debate: namely, how to handle the thousands of patients already ventilator-dependent in chronic-care facilities. Powell's committee chose to consider acute and chronic patients separately, rather than "assessing all intubated patients, whether in acute or chronic care facilities, by the same set of criteria." The group acknowledged that commandeering chronic-care ventilators might lead to more survivors, but noted "they would also be different types of survivors." Under this alternative approach, the disabled would be sacrificed for the greater good.

Powell's group and like-minded ethicists fear that removing patients from chronic ventilator support reflects judgments based on third-party assessments of quality of life—the same sort of judgments that had been used with disturbing results at Seattle's Swedish Hospital in the 1960s, where people of perceived social worth were favored for scarce dialysis treatments. Critics counter that excluding those with chronic disabilities from the assessment pool actually shows irrational bias *toward* the disabled. They argue that, once personal considerations are excluded, most people would prefer a triage system that saves the largest number of lives possible.

61

A Cheaper Knockoff

SEVERAL NEW MEDICATIONS for hepatitis C, a disease that often leads to liver failure and cancer, are available on the market. These new medications have many fewer side effects than older, interferon-based medications, which can cause debilitating psychiatric symptoms. However, the manufacturers charge more than $50,000 for a twelve-week course of treatment. ProfitMeds owns a patent on the medication and has spent nearly $100 million to develop it. CheapMeds, a company in India, has reverse engineered one of these medications and has started to market it for $1 a pill—making the entire cost of treatment available for $84.

Is CheapMeds doing anything wrong?

REFLECTION: Intellectual Property

INTELLECTUAL PROPERTY LAWS are designed to create incentives for innovation. Patents for pharmaceuticals in the United States generally last for twenty years, giving manufacturers the exclusive right to profit from their research investment in new drugs.

After that, other companies are permitted to market generic versions of a drug, but generics also require receiving regulatory approval from the Food and Drug Administration—a costly and time-consuming endeavor. Notorious pharmaceutical entrepreneur Martin Shkreli exploited this process in 2015 when his company bought the rights to an off-patent medication for the treatment of toxoplasmosis—pyrimethamine (Daraprim)—for which no generic version was yet available, and raised the price by 5,556 percent. (Shkreli was later convicted of securities fraud in a different matter and sentenced to seven years in federal prison.)

The twenty-year monopolies themselves can also render some novel drugs extremely expensive. Genentech's anticancer agent Avastin initially ran patients up to $100,000 annually, although the price has since fallen to $24,000. Gilead's hepatitis treatment Harvoni costs $94,500 for a twelve-week course. Needless to say, these medications are well out of reach of many US healthcare consumers in the US, not to mention most patients in the developing world. Even less expensive treatments are unaffordable to indigent populations in Asia, Africa, and Latin America. To address these concerns, several developing nations have shaped their intellectual property laws in ways so that local manufacturers can produce these same medications at much lower costs.

Until 2005, several nations—most notably India—permitted local companies like Mumbai-based Cipla to engage in the reverse engineering of pharmaceuticals. Under Indian law, patents were granted for processes, rather than products. Finding an alternative route to the same drug enabled local manufacturers to flood the market with low-priced "knockoffs." Critics derided these manufacturers as "pirates," accusing them of stealing profits from the rightful owners. Defenders, including many healthcare NGOs, countered that the individuals who purchased these "knockoffs" would not have bought the drugs at the higher prices anyway. Eventually, to comply with the international Agreement on Trade-Related Aspects of Intellectual Property Rights, better known as TRIPS, India prohibited this practice. However, India continues to find ways to circumvent Western patient protections to make and export generic drugs at low cost.

One method used by India's government is compulsory licensing, a process permitted by TRIPS that allows nations to grant companies the right to produce products already under patent, in certain circumstances, if the patent holders are appropriately compensated. Under Indian law, "compulsory license shall be available for manufacture and export of patented pharmaceutical products to any country having insufficient or no manufacturing capacity in the pharmaceutical sector for the concerned product to address public health problems." The first such license in India was granted for Bayer's kidney cancer drug Nexavar (sorafenib) in 2012.

An ideal patent system would permit precisely the amount of protection needed to ensure the balance between research and access that would save the most lives. Finding that theoretical balancing point might prove impossible in a perfect world—and is certainly unlikely to occur in the political context of conflict between large pharmaceutical companies and the health ministries of powerful developing nations. For many years, this conflict has played out largely on the international stage; as increasingly expensive drugs have come to market in the United States, this is becoming a domestic political issue as well. New hepatitis C drugs cost Medicare $4.5 billion in 2014—more than fifteen times the amount it spent on older, interferon-based drugs in 2013. Many bioethicists and health-care policy makers are now asking which patients should be entitled to drugs like Harvoni and its sister drug, Sovaldi, while others are asking whether the government should intervene directly to reduce the costs.

62

No Black Sperm Donors
Need Apply

BLANCHE'S SPERM BANK pays various rates to sperm donors based on their age and the degree of health information they are willing to provide. The enterprise excludes donors with certain diseases, family histories of genetic illness, or those below a specific height. "Nobody pays for sperm from short men," Blanche says candidly.

One day, looking over the sperm bank's recent supply and demand, she decides that she is no longer going to accept African American sperm donors. "I'm sorry," she tells prospective black donors. "The demand just isn't there. We don't have many Caucasian women seeking dark-skinned sperm donors, and in this neighborhood, ninety-nine percent of our clientele is white." She places a sign on her door that reads NO AFRICAN AMERICAN DONORS. SORRY.

SHOULD BLANCHE BE ALLOWED TO REFUSE SPERM FROM AFRICAN AMERICAN DONORS?

REFLECTION: The Business of Reproduction

SPERM BANKS, LIKE all other businesses operating in a market, are vulnerable to the economic forces of supply and demand. These forces can often vary considerably by region, nation, and culture. For example, the world's largest sperm purveyor, Copenhagen-based Cryos International, made headlines in 2011 when it declared a moratorium on redheaded donors. The firm's founder, Ole Schou, reportedly told the Danish daily *Ekstra Bladet*, "There are too many redheads in relation to demand." Danes apparently prefer semen from men with dark hair and eyes. In contrast, red-headed donors remain in high demand in Ireland.

Personal preferences can run deep. In 2014, Jennifer Cramblett of Ohio filed suit for "wrongful birth" and "breach of warranty" against a sperm bank that had accidentally sent her sperm from an African American donor; Cramblett, who is white, gave birth to a healthy biracial baby girl. The case was ultimately dismissed by a state court in 2015.

In Blanche's scenario, the law can address the predicament in one of two ways: it can allow her to respond to market forces and refuse to pay African American donors, or it can compel her to continue to pay African American donors—knowing that their sperm will go unused but declaring that such wasted semen is simply a cost of doing business and a necessary, albeit inconvenient, by-product of living in a nondiscriminatory society. Any third alternative aimed at altering the underlying market forces, such as denying recipients the right to choose the race of their sperm, would likely prove politically unpalatable and economically unviable, at least in the short term—no matter how just it might appear in theory.

With regard to selecting donors, sperm banks remain largely unregulated in the United States. Their status under civil rights laws has never been fully clarified. Are they more like a restaurant or a store, legally and ethically required both to employ and to serve individuals of all races? Or is donating sperm more like joining a private club? And even if civil rights laws apply, does consumer demand in this distinctive field create a compelling exception to the general rule favoring race-neutral hiring? A Shakespearean theater need not audition white actors for the part of Othello. Maybe a similar exception ought to apply regarding sperm donation.

At least one effort has been made to create a "whites-only" sperm bank; in 1996, billionaires Floyd and Doris Kimble opened a Washington State sperm bank that refused to accept donations from African Americans. And until 2013, Calgary's Regional Fertility Program—a private sperm repository— permitted recipients to choose donors of only their own race.

Whether or not Blanche's sign is legal or ethical, it may have an unexpected effect on her business: one can imagine many white customers, seeking white sperm, who nonetheless feel uncomfortable, or downright unwilling, to patronize a business with a no african american donors sign out front.

63

"She Can Share a Room with a Man"

St. Dymphna's Hospital is a small 120-bed hospital serving a predominantly rural population. Phil brings his elderly aunt Jenny to the emergency room after she suffers shortness of breath. She is diagnosed with pneumonia and told she will be admitted to the hospital as soon as a bed becomes available. Forty-eight hours later, on Sunday night, she is still waiting in the crowded emergency room, because the hospital is reportedly full.

Phil is a vigilant observer, and he notes that his aunt has been waiting longer than any other patient. He overhears one of the senior nurse managers, Ms. Rached, on the phone discussing the "bed situation." She says: "They're telling me we have an open bed for a male patient, but none for any female patients until someone is discharged." Phil approaches the nurse manager and says, "My aunt is ninety-two years old and very ill. I don't care if she's in a room with a man or a woman. We'll just draw the curtain. I want the first bed available." The nearest other hospital with available beds is more than six hours away by ambulance.

No law prevents Ms. Rached from admitting a female patient

to a double room already occupied by a male patient. However, in practice, the hospital has never allowed "coed" hospital rooms before, and, since it is Sunday night, Ms. Rached is the highest-ranking administrator on-site. She calls upstairs and learns that the male patient in the room with the available bed is a ninety-one-year-old double amputee in a coma. No family is involved in his care.

Should Ms. Rached make an exception to the historic practice of the hospital and temporarily admit Aunt Jenny to a room with a male patient, or should Aunt Jenny be asked to wait until a "female room" becomes available?

<hr />

REFLECTION: Gender-Blind Hospital Rooms

SINGLE-GENDER HOSPITAL ROOMS have historically been the norm in the United States. Exceptions include emergency rooms and intensive care units, which are well trafficked and generally make no effort to segregate men and women. Such separation serves no medical purpose. In fact, when hospitals are crowded, it can delay admissions to the medical floors from the emergency room. However, single-gender hospital rooms comply with the customs of a large segment of society, and some people may be uncomfortable sharing a room with a patient of another sex. Parts of Canada, most notably Alberta, have permitted coed hospital rooms since 2005. Such a policy can operate in three distinct ways: (1) all patients can be compelled to accept the first room available, no matter what the gender of the other occupant; (2) patients can be assigned to gender-blind rooms unless they overtly object to sharing a room with a person of the opposite gender; or (3) patients can be asked their preferences on the matter without prompting, and only those who express their willingness will be assigned to gender-blind rooms.

Opponents of gender-blind rooms often resort to arguments based on tradition or what is known as "the wisdom of repugnance," a term coined by Leon Kass to explain things that are considered to be morally wrong even if it is difficult to articulate *why* they are morally wrong. Sometimes this is referred to as the "yuck factor." Similar arguments, often cloaked in religion, are used in some nations to keep women and men from sitting together at weddings or on buses. Other opponents of coed rooms express fears for the safety of female patients, including the prospect of sexual assault, although no such cases have been reported in facilities that have adopted this approach. (Similar objections are frequently raised by those who oppose allowing transgender individuals to use restrooms that match their gender identities.) No safety concerns are unlikely to apply in cases like Aunt Jenny's, where the male patient is comatose.

In cases where both parties are willing, one is hard-pressed to advance a plausible argument against such arrangements. A more complex situation arises where one of the patients is willing but the other patient is not able to express a preference—such as in Ms. Rached's dilemma. In short, she is asked to decide what the default option should be in the absence of either objection or consent from the patient.

One other factor should play into Ms. Rached's thinking. She must decide to what degree to rely upon long-standing policies and when to carve out an exception based upon distinctive circumstances. Hard-and-fast rules may mete out injustices on occasion, but they ensure a uniform fairness in the application of controversial policies. Those who argue for such rigid standards value the rule of law and would want the hospital to change its policy rather than to permit Ms. Rached to single-handedly circumvent it. In contrast, allowing for discretion often achieves justice in the short run but may permit arbitrary decisions in other cases or may set troublesome precedents that lead to injustice in the future. In addition to deciding whether admitting Aunt Jenny to a male patient's room is the right thing to do at the moment, Ms. Rached must decide whether doing so is worth the consequences of such a decision for other patients in the future.

64

Healthy Workers Only

A PRIVATE HOSPITAL is concerned that smoking and obesity among its employees are driving up its healthcare costs. The hospital board enacts a new employment policy: all new hires must refrain from smoking and must maintain a healthy body weight. The facility plans to conduct random urine tests twice each year to screen for nicotine and to conduct annual weigh-ins. All employees found in violation of hospital policy will be given one warning and an opportunity to engage in smoking-cessation and weight-loss programs. If they again fail to meet either standard, they will be dismissed.

Should this policy be legal?

REFLECTION: Employee Rights

THE CENTERS FOR Disease Control estimates that tobacco smoking costs the US economy more than $300 billion annually, while a 2012 study in the *Journal of Health Economics* attributes 21 percent of the nation's healthcare costs to obesity. Much of this burden falls upon employers through increased insurance premiums and lost worker productivity. In an effort to avoid such expenditures, businesses and nonprofit organizations have increasingly turned to "tobacco-free" and "healthy-weight" hiring policies. When several large US corporations—including Alaska Airlines—stopped hiring smokers in the 1980s, a backlash led twenty-nine states to pass right-to-work laws for tobacco users, although many included exceptions for healthcare institutions and nonprofits. A range of entities, from hospitals to fire departments, have since adopted such restrictions and have met with little resistance. Citizens Medical Center in Victoria, Texas, now requires all new hires to have body mass indexes under 35 (normal weight is a BMI of 18.5 to 25). These policies raise fundamental questions about the balance between the prerogatives of employers and the privacy rights of employees.

Arguably, one of the major benefits of modern work life is its inability to reach into the home. Most employees no longer live in "company towns"; their bosses do not track their church attendance or regulate with whom they fraternize. Yet the rise of social media, such as Facebook and Twitter, has eroded some of these barriers. In an effort to protect their own images, companies can—and sometimes do—fire workers who post offensive statements online. Regulating employee health reflects another way in which public-private barriers are breaking down. In addition to economic concerns, employers may have genuine worries about the public image conveyed by an unhealthy employee, such as a physician or a nurse who posts photographs of herself smoking cigarettes on the internet.

What some well-intentioned individuals view as an attempt to encourage healthy living, critics see as an effort to demonize those who live unhealthy lives. Opponents also express fears that such policies will fall disproportionately upon low-wage workers. In fact, the *New York Times* reported that of the first fourteen applications turned down for positions at University Medical Center of El Paso under a smoke-free hiring policy, "one was applying to be a nurse and the rest for support positions." After a European Union court ruled in favor of Karsten Kaltoft, a childcare worker who claimed obesity to be a disability, was fired for his weight, a British study revealed that nearly half of one thousand British employers would not hire overweight applicants, often believing them to be lazy and incompetent. Policies like that proposed by the hospital in the scenario at the start of the chapter risk furthering such stereotypes.

These issues have proven among the most divisive in healthcare—often pitting leading advocacy groups against each other. For example, the American Lung Association and the American Cancer Society refuse to hire smokers; in contrast, another major antismoking organization, the American Legacy Foundation (ALF), strongly opposes such policies. As the ALF's chief counsel told the *New York Times* in 2011, "We want to be very supportive of smokers, and the best thing we can do is help them quit, not condition employment on whether they quit. Smokers are not the enemy."

65

Will I Get Alzheimer's?

LOIS IS AN investigative reporter for a major newspaper. Her editor, Paul, asks her to write a story on genetic testing for Alzheimer's disease. Paul has read that there is a genetic test that can reveal whether one has an elevated risk of suffering from this form of dementia in later life. He wants Lois to undergo the test and print her results in the newspaper.

Lois learns that a person inherits half of her known genetic risk for the disease from each parent through what are called APOE genes—and that this accounts for some, but not all, of a person's risk of developing Alzheimer's disease in old age. That means that learning one's own risk, if it is high, can also reveal, or "unmask," whether one's parents stand at risk. Lois is only twenty-eight years old, and her parents, both in their fifties, are still living. Fortunately, they reside in a distant city and rarely read her newspaper columns.

Is it ethical for Lois to publish her test results, allowing for the prospect that her parents will somehow learn of these results and possibly their own increased risk of this incurable, debilitating ailment?

REFLECTION: Genetic Testing and Privacy

ALZHEIMER'S DISEASE, WHICH affects more than five million predominantly elderly Americans, remains one of the most feared diagnoses anyone can receive. Treatments are limited and merely slow the inevitable progression toward dementia and death. APOE gene status reveals a percentage of the likelihood of developing the disease; individuals carrying two high-risk variants of the gene (known as APOE4s) are approximately fifteen times more likely to develop Alzheimer's disease than those with two average-risk variants (known as APOE3s). Yet unlike with more traditional genetic conditions, such as cystic fibrosis or muscular dystrophy, where the genetic mutation automatically leads to the disease, the results for Alzheimer's are not carved in stone. Some patients with two APOE4 alleles remain cognitively intact into old age. Some patients with two APOE3 alleles develop Alzheimer's disease. Scientists do not yet know why.

Now that commercial testing is available for APOE status, some people choose to avail themselves of this information. Ethicists have expressed concerns that patients who learn of their high-risk status may suffer unnecessary psychiatric consequences, such as depression. However, data from Huntington's disease patients suggests that positive genetic testing does not actually lead to higher rates of depression or suicide. Rather, it may afford relief (whether merited or not) to some, while allowing others to plan ahead for their future health. (Of note, I had my APOE genes tested for Alzheimer's risk, which turns out to be average, and have written about my experience.) Yet prominent scientists, including psychologist Steven Pinker and geneticist James Watson, have insisted on not finding out their APOE status even while revealing the remainder of their genomes to the public. Nonetheless, in a rather concerning article in the *European Journal of Human Genetics*, geneticist Dale Nyholt and others reported that Watson's status could likely be predicted on the basis of other DNA markers he had made available.

Lois faces a more challenging dilemma than merely determining her own status. She must also decide whether to share her status in such a way that doing so could affect her parents. Such unmasking is a common risk with many genetic disorders. Family members have little recourse to prevent such disclosure—even though it can have significant repercussions for their own lives. Some commentators have raised the possibility that in cases of rare, incurable genetic disorders, such as Machado-Joseph disease, the community of patients might deserve a say in whether researchers ever develop a genetic test for the disease in the first place. If no test exists, there is no risk of unmasking. For more common diseases like Alzheimer's, such a majority veto or "majority right not to know" is not realistically feasible.

66

"I Want to Live to Meet My Child"

WILBERT IS A thirty-year-old man with a newly diagnosed pancreatic tumor. His wife is three months pregnant, and there is the possibility, estimated at 10 percent, that an extremely expensive new drug will extend his life long enough for him to witness the birth of his first child. He relies on Medicaid for his healthcare coverage and cannot afford private insurance.

The leaders of the state in which Wilbert resides have recently passed legislation that prevents its Medicaid program from paying for chemotherapy for patients with under a 5 percent chance of surviving five years. The funds saved have been earmarked for preventive medicine, expanding such coverage to one hundred thousand working-class children. Economists estimate this approach will save hundreds of lives every year. In agreeing to the law, the governor required the state legislature to establish an emergency review board—a three-member commission that can override these rules and provide funding for such chemotherapy under "extraordinary circumstances." Wilbert petitions the board for an exception. He writes: "I know my chances of long-term survival are extremely low, but I have a realistic prospect of living to see my first child born—and that would mean the world to me and my family."

Should the emergency review board authorize an emergency override in this case?

<hr>

REFLECTION: Healthcare Rationing

HEALTHCARE RATIONING, IN some form or another, is unavoidable. The alternative—covering all possible healthcare costs for every living American—would vastly increase the percentage of gross national product devoted to medicine at the expense of other vital budget items, such as education, defense, or consumer goods. Such a dramatic spike in expenditures would likely prove politically intolerable. Instead, as columnist David Leonhardt wrote in the *New York Times*, "The choice isn't between rationing and not rationing. It's between rationing well and rationing badly." At present, our system rations badly. Princeton University's Peter Singer, in another *New York Times* column, compared the cases of patients refused extremely expensive kidney cancer treatments by their insurers, denials which drew national outrage, with that of a woman from Atlanta who suffered from a ruptured brain aneurysm because she could not afford a relatively inexpensive blood-pressure medication. Logically, whatever total funding society wishes to expend on prevention and treatment, common sense suggests paying for the Atlanta woman's medication before that of the kidney cancer patients.

Oregon implemented a "rational" system of partial rationing in the 1990s that remains in effect. Led by then-governor John Kitzhaber, a former emergency room physician, the state decided to expand the number of working-poor patients eligible for Medicaid. In order to do this, with limited funds, the state stopped paying for certain expensive treatments under the same program. Healthcare economists estimated that, in the long run, this approach would save lives and improve overall well-being through increased preventive care and expanded access. Yet such a system created "visible" victims, who suffered the short-term consequences necessary for society's long-term benefit. In 2008, lung cancer patient Barbara Wagner's request for the drug Tarceva, which cost $4,000 a month, was rejected by the Oregon Health Plan. Kenneth Stevens Jr., of the Physicians for Compassionate Care Education Foundation, reports that according to Oregon's rules, Medicaid "will not cover the cost of surgery, radiotherapy or chemotherapy for patients with a less than 5% expected 5-year-survival." The media and conservative organizations drew attention to the ironic fact that while Wagner could not receive cancer treatments, she was eligible for state-funded palliative care and physician-assisted suicide. (The drugmaker Genentech agreed to provide Tarceva for free; Wagner died in October 2008, shortly after her first dose.)

Other states have experimented with some forms of limited rationing. Massachusetts, in the 1980s, and Arizona, in 2011, denied funding for certain organ transplants—until high-profile media portrayals of people excluded, such as that of dying infant Jamie Fiske, pressured the states to alter their policies. In Wilbert's scenario, he may have a compelling case for treatment, but if he is granted an exception to see the birth of his son, other patients will likely step forward with equally compelling cases. Helping these "identified patients" will—in the long run—cost the lives of others, like the Atlanta woman who suffered the devastating brain aneurysm.

In 1984, economist Lester Thurow, writing in the *New England Journal of Medicine*, explained the fundamental challenge of the US healthcare system in the following way: "As libertarians, Americans are unwilling to deny any particular medication or procedure to wealthy people who can afford to pay for it on their own. Yet as egalitarians, once we allow some patients to obtain a medical intervention, we feel obligated to make that same treatment available to everyone—regardless of cost. The results are rising expenditures and irrational forms of rationing that favor visible patients over invisible victims." Carving out an exception to Wilbert's state's rationing system would produce precisely that unappealing trade-off.

67

Pills for Peak Performance

DR. LYDGATE IS a neurologist in private practice. One of her longtime patients, an airplane pilot named Camille, requests that she prescribe her a stimulant, Big A, that is usually given only to patients with rare sleep disorders and narcolepsy. "All of the other pilots take it," Camille explains. "It helps us concentrate better when we're in the air."

Anecdotally, Dr. Lydgate has heard from her colleagues of similar requests, and she knows that stimulants generally can improve short-term focus. Yet the medication has never been approved for this purpose and Camille is not suffering from any known neurological or concentration disorder. In short, she is asking for a medication to enhance her abilities to levels above normal rather than to correct a defect. Dr. Lydgate is confident that Camille's risk for addiction is very low and that she is telling her the truth about the reason for her request.

Should Dr. Lydgate prescribe Big A to Camille?

REFLECTION: Cognitive Enhancement

NOOTROPICS ARE MEDICATIONS that improve cognitive performance in various ways. These might include improvements in memory, arousal, and concentration. Some, including caffeine, are already in widespread use. Others, such as the stimulant Adderall and the wakefulness-promoting agent modafinil, are available only through a prescription or on the extensive black market. For certain individuals, notably patients with attention deficit hyperactivity disorder (ADHD) or narcolepsy, nootropics help treat their illnesses and allow them to function at the level of their peers. For others, these same medications are believed to—and sometimes do—improve performance above the norm. Yet the line between therapy and enhancement is a blurry one.

In many settings, the use of performance-enhancing drugs may be viewed as "cheating." For instance, much as baseball players are not allowed to inject steroids, some ethicists argue that using amphetamines to study for the SAT gives students an unfair advantage. Critics, of course, note that there are a host of unfair advantages related to SAT preparation that certain students possess and others so not. Wealthy students hire tutors, do not have to work jobs that cut into study time, and can more easily find quiet places to learn without distraction. Why should one prohibit nootropic use but not SAT tutors? Of course, SAT tutors impose very little medical risk. In contrast, amphetamines pose a wide variety of risks and side effects, including addiction potential. These risks might justify banning the use of such drugs for enhancement, but it is a mistake to conflate this argument about danger with concern for unfair advantages.

Probably the most significant threat posed by nootropics is the potential that patients will feel pressured or forced to use them. From Camille's encounter with Dr. Lydgate, it appears that Big A use is now expected of certain pilots—including those who might not want to assume the long-term medical risks of taking the medication. One woman's ceiling, as the expression goes, is another woman's floor. If widespread Big A use raises the performance standards for pilots to a level where nonusers cannot compete, anyone interested in flying commercial jets will be forced, in practice, to opt for cognitive enhancement. Nootropics have the potential to create a "new normal," against which all participants will be judged. That might prove problematic for a prospective airplane pilot, but it might also be somewhat reassuring to a potential passenger, should it turn out that these agents actually do render air travel safer.

68

"I'd Rather Be Psychotic Than Stupid"

CAROLINA IS A sixty-year-old woman with a history of schizophrenia. She has been admitted to psychiatric hospitals more than thirty times for paranoia, auditory hallucinations, and bizarre behavior. Often, once she is stabilized on medication, her symptoms resolve and she is able to return to the group home where she lives. Yet the medications make Carolina feel "numb" and "stupid," and she is unwilling to take them voluntarily. "I'd rather be psychotic than stupid," she tells one of her psychiatrists.

One time immediately after being discharged from the hospital, when she is still on medication and asymptomatic, Carolina finds a lawyer who helps her draft a document called a "psychiatric advance directive." In the document, she affirms that if she again becomes psychotic, she does not want to receive any medication. She is willing to let the state hospitalize her permanently, if need be, to protect the public and prevent her from self-harm, but she says she does not want to be medicated under any circumstances. She also records a video to go along with the document. "Please don't believe me if I change my mind," she says on the video. "When I'm in the hospital, sometimes I'll say or do anything to get out. But that's not the real me speaking." Carolina's lawyer arranges for two psychiatrists to evaluate her at the time she signs the document. These psychiatric evaluations are preserved on video. Both evaluators agree that she is asymptomatic and thinking rationally.

As soon as the document is signed, Carolina stops taking her medications and becomes psychotic again. She is taken to a psychiatric hospital where the doctors seek a court order to medicate her forcibly. There is no clear legal precedent on the subject in this jurisdiction.

Should the court honor Carolina's document, or should the doctors be allowed to medicate her?

REFLECTION: **Psychiatric Advance Directives**

ADVANCE DIRECTIVES (ADs) for medical decision-making, first proposed by Amnesty International cofounder Luis Kutner in 1969, have become a staple of modern healthcare. California became the first state to authorize such documents in 1976; today, every state has such a statute. In the Patient Self-Determination Act of 1990, Congress required hospitals to educate patients on ADs. These documents, which often take the form of living wills, specify how patients wish their medical care to be handled if they lose the capacity to make their own decisions.

More recently, mental health professionals have grappled with how to translate the principles underlying ADs—patient autonomy and empowerment—into the psychiatric setting. As of 2018, a majority of states have statutes authorizing psychiatric advance directives (PADs) in some form or another. Yet PADs are underutilized. According to psychologist Heather Zelle and her colleagues, "66%–77% of consumers would complete a psychiatric advance directive if given the opportunity and assistance; however, only 4%–13% actually have completed one." In most jurisdictions, PADs are not binding; unlike medical ADs, they merely guide care and can be overridden by psychiatrists or courts.

The judge in Carolina's case is being asked to decide whether her PAD should be legally binding. Documents that are binding in the future, even if the person creating the document attempts to change her mind, are often called "Ulysses contracts" after the hero of Homer's *Odyssey*. In the Greek epic, Odysseus (a.k.a. Ulysses) has himself bound to his ship's mast, so that he can hear the music of the mythical beauties the Sirens, and commands his crew not to release him—even if he eventually begs them to do so. Similarly, Carolina wishes to be bound by a document she previously executed, even if she later wishes to revoke it.

One US patient has already won a legal battle to have her PAD upheld under these circumstances. Nancy Hargrave, a women with paranoid schizophrenia hospitalized at the Vermont State Hospital, executed a durable power of attorney stating that she did not want nonemergency psychiatric medication. Her PAD was upheld by the US Second Circuit Court of Appeals in 2003. The state did not appeal further.

Critics of binding PADs often argue that psychiatric patients may not appreciate the full effect of entering into a Ulysses contract and that their wishes may genuinely evolve. Yet Duke University psychiatry professor Jeffrey Swanson and his colleagues noted in 2006 that the rationale for PADs may be stronger than for ADs for general medical patients: "From the perspective of patients with a long history of psychiatric treatment, PADs may actually convey treatment preferences much more accurately than medical advance directives or living wills do, to the extent that such preferences are shaped by previous personal encounters with the health care interventions in question." At the same time, psychiatric hospitalization is costly. A patient whose PAD rejects medication or electroconvulsive therapy but who cannot survive safely in the community without such treatments, is essentially asking the taxpayers to fund her indefinite confinement. With the mental health system perennially starved for resources, one wonders whether such an extreme effort to uphold patient autonomy—no matter how well intended—is worth the tangible costs.

69

Hazardous Hobbies

THE US GOVERNMENT is concerned about the healthcare costs of individuals engaged in purely volitional high-risk behaviors such as motorcycle riding, hang gliding, and bungee jumping. While injuries from such activities are not all that common, they often prove very costly. Senator Cheapside has proposed legislation to prevent all government-run insurance programs, including Medicare and Medicaid, from paying for healthcare costs resulting directly from these activities. He has identified ninety-two other activities not to be covered as well—ranging from amateur beekeeping to illegal drag racing. "If you want to be insured for injuries you acquire while engaged in high-risk activities," he says, "you should purchase private insurance to cover your costs."

Should Senator Cheapside's approach to deterring high-risk behaviors be adopted?

REFLECTION: The Cost of Risk

LIFE INSURERS GENERALLY charge a premium for high-risk behaviors. According to a 2013 article in *U.S. News & World Report*, hunters pay an additional $500 annual premium, and rock climbers pay $1,500 extra; scuba diving and skydiving can add $2,500 to one's rates. Health insurers do not always dig as deeply into the personal behavior of policyholders, but some refuse to cover individuals engaged in dangerous activities. In 2006, one major Illinois corporation reportedly sent letters to its employees informing them that any motorcycle-related injuries would result in immediate termination of their health insurance. In contrast, Medicare and Medicaid usually cover all injuries of their clients, regardless of the origins of those injuries.

The primary reason that public health-insurance entities do not exclude these risk-takers is that health insurance no longer functions as insurance—at least, not in the traditional sense. As political historian Edward N. Beiser observed in the article "The Emperor's New Scrubs" (1994), "health insurance" is a misnomer. The underlying principle behind traditional insurance is the distribution or "pooling" of risk. Although the odds of my house burning down are quite low, the odds of somebody's home catching fire are reasonably high, and fire insurance evenly distributes the cost of this burden. Everyone pays in; a few unlucky victims receive compensation. In contrast, the vast majority of Americans will eventually experience injuries or illnesses beyond the age of sixty-five, so nearly all of us will withdraw resources from Medicare. Rather than an insurance program, Medicare is a resource management program, through which, in theory, workers fork over their money to the government, which stores it for them and returns it later to pay for their medical expenses (although the reality is that current payroll taxes pay for today's elderly, while future workers will supposedly pay for today's workers to receive coverage).

Since Medicare and Medicaid are default systems for healthcare coverage—filling in for the poor and elderly where private insurance historically did not pay—refusing insurance for high-risk behaviors will leave a pool of injured patients without any way to pay for emergency treatment. As a result of a federal statute, the Emergency Medical Treatment and Labor Act of 1986 (EMTALA), hospitals cannot legally turn such patients away. Moreover, even if hospitals could legally opt out of this care, refusing services in an urgent setting is morally indefensible. So rather than deterring conduct or conserving resources, Senator Cheapside's approach would likely just shift the price tag for such care to hospitals, which would then pass this cost along to consumers through higher medical bills.

Another possible problem with Senator Cheapside's proposal is that it may save Medicare and Medicaid less money than he anticipates. Few people who have incomes low enough to qualify to receive Medicaid are likely engaged in beekeeping, bungee jumping, or many of the other expensive activities that concern him. Nor are many elderly Americans, who benefit from Medicare, hang gliding for sport. By far the greatest preventable expenditures for the healthcare system are those related to more mundane risks—namely obesity and cigarette smoking. Arguably, one might deter smoking and excessive eating by refusing to pay for medical conditions resulting from this conduct. Yet that approach would punish overeaters and addicts for health woes that may prove beyond their control and might even sentence them to worsening illness or death.

70

Sex in the Nursing Home

RILEY AND NORMA are two elderly residents of the dementia unit at the Shady Acres Nursing Home. Both suffer from Alzheimer's disease and are profoundly impaired—generally unable to recognize friends and family or to accomplish more than the most basic tasks. In addition, Norma has numerous outbursts daily, likely tied to anxiety and paranoia. Both of their spouses are deceased; their children live in distant states, check in infrequently, and never visit.

One week, the staff at Shady Acres notices a profound change in Norma. She is calmer and less paranoid. Six days elapse without an outburst. The staff soon discovers a possible cause: Riley has been sneaking into Norma's room each night after lights-out, and the couple has been engaging in sexual intercourse. It appears Riley has mistaken Norma for his late wife. Although neither Riley nor Norma have the capacity to consent to sex in the way of people without cognitive impairment, they both seem to find the experience soothing and therapeutic.

Assuming there is no risk of spreading disease and only a minimal risk of injury, should the staff allow Riley and Norma to continue their sexual encounters?

REFLECTION: Dementia and Consent

SEX AMONG THE elderly, and particularly among elderly patients suffering from dementia, has long been a taboo subject in the United States. This contrasts with some European nations, such as Denmark, where Copenhagen's Thorupgaarden nursing home makes pornography and prostitutes available to residents. In US facilities, sexuality is more likely to be met with concern or even derision. This proves especially true with cognitively impaired patients. In 1996, an Ohio court denied a husband overnight nursing home visits with his stroke-afflicted wife for fear that he might seek "sexual intimacy" with her—and that this might lead to litigation for the facility. A seventy-eight-year-old former Iowa state legislator, Henry Rayhons, briefly made national headlines when prosecutors tried him for sexual activity with his elderly wife, who suffered from Alzheimer's disease. Prosecutors argued that Donna Rayhons lacked the capacity to consent, but the jury acquitted her husband of all charges. Only a few US nursing homes, such as the Hebrew Home at Riverdale, have proactive policies legitimizing and governing sex between patients.

One challenge in dementia cases is the issue of consent. Yet consent—with its formal standards—is a problematic concept when speaking of impaired patients. Elderly patients with dementia do not "consent" (in the legal sense) to many things—having their blood pressure checked, showering and changing clothes, eating. Rather, they often "assent" to such activities, either by smiling or expressing enthusiasm or merely offering no resistance, even when they may not fully understand what they are doing or why. Sexual activity is obviously more complicated than merely eating or watching television, and one certainly wants to protect vulnerable patients from truly involuntary sexual activity that amounts to sexual assault. *Slate* columnist Daniel Engber has raised the possibility of "formal exceptions to the consent rules for spouses or long-term partners." Rather, one might merely require assent in such cases—evidence that that patient is willing to engage in the behavior and appears to enjoy it.

More complex are cases of two elderly individuals with dementia, like Norma and Riley, who seek sexual activity with one another and appear to benefit from it. How to preserve both safety and dignity for these residents under such circumstances is a challenge, but not one that necessarily justifies enforced chastity. The feeling and wishes of third parties, such as the patient's spouses and children, may also prove a concern. Should Norma and Riley's nursing home inform their families about their relationship? Should their children have any say in whether the relations are permitted to continue? In one high-profile instance, the *New York Times* reported on the romance between former Supreme Court justice Sandra Day O'Connor's cognitively impaired husband and another cognitively impaired resident at his assisted living facility—although it did not explicitly touch upon their sex lives. Justice O'Connor, ever graceful under stress, appeared supportive. One can easily imagine another spouse feeling less sympathetic.

PART SIX

End-of-Life Issues

The field of bioethics emerged as its own discipline in the 1960s and 1970s largely around issues related to death and dying. Prior to this era, the boundaries between life and death were generally clear—although controversies did arise surrounding the return of individuals lost and presumed dead. (One of the best-known of these cases, the legend of sixteenth-century French peasant-turned-solider Martin Guerre, became the subject of literature and film.) When one's heart stopped beating and one's lungs stopped breathing, a person was considered dead. The advent of mechanical respirators in the late 1950s complicated that definition, as a machine could keep human lungs breathing through artificial means long after they could no longer do so on their own. The question became, Were such patients alive? And if so, what standard for death should replace the traditional cardiopulmonary version?

These questions were debated among professionals, starting in France, where a team of neurophysiologists first sought to define *coma dépassé* in 1958, and mostly notably, by leading experts who formed a committee at Harvard Medical School on the definition of "brain death" and "irreversible coma" in the 1960s. High-profile cases like that of Karen Ann Quinlan, a young woman in a persistent vegetative state whose parents sought to have her removed from a ventilator, brought the debate into US living rooms in the 1970s. Eventually, the federal government became involved, and a presidential commission published a seminal report on the subject in the early 1980s. Unfortunately, time has brought society no closer to a consensus on many of the ethical questions related to the end of life: What definition of death should medicine embrace? How should we handle patients or families who disagree with that standard? Should the medical community help people end their own lives when they are suffering?

71

Who Says You're Dead?

ENOCH IS A five-year-old Mennonite baby with a terminal brain tumor. He is a patient at a small hospital in his rural community. As his condition deteriorates, he is placed on a ventilator, and he soon loses consciousness. Eventually, his doctors conduct a series of tests known as electroencephalograms and conclude that his brain function has completely ceased. Under state law, Enoch is now dead.

Enoch's parents, Jared and Susanna, do not believe in brain death. According to their traditions, a person is not dead as long as the heart is still beating. "Under your rules, he may be dead," says Jared. "To my family, he is very much alive." They insist that the doctors care for their child indefinitely. When the hospital refuses, they raise money in their community to purchase a ventilator so that they can care for Enoch in their own living room.

Should Jared and Susanna be permitted to take this child, who is legally dead, home with them on "life support?"

REFLECTION: Defining Death

UNTIL THE SECOND half of the twentieth century, most legal systems defined "death" as the cessation of heartbeat, the cessation of breathing, or both—hence the iconic image of the nineteenth-century physician holding up a mirror to the mouth of a cadaver to check for vapor from the patient's breath. These standards proved problematic with the development of artificial methods of respiration, such as ventilators, and later with the invention of ventricular assist devices (VADs) to help pump blood. Such machines allow a patient with no brain function or prognosis for recovery to remain "alive" (under the cardio-pulmonary definition of death) for an extended period of time while hooked up to medical equipment.

Starting in 1968 with the report from the Ad Hoc Committee of the Harvard Medical School, the concept of "brain death" or "whole brain death" gained social and legal traction in the United States. In 1981, a presidential commission initially appointed by Jimmy Carter issued a report, *Defining Death: Medical, Legal and Ethical Issues in the Determination of Death*, which urged states to adopt the "whole brain death" standard. A majority of states have done so. (An alternative approach, that asks whether a patient retains "higher" brain functions, such as the ability to think, has been largely rejected.)

While most Americans now accept brain death, some cultural and religious minorities reject this new criterion. In several high-profile cases—including those of Mordechai Dov Brody (1996–2008), an Orthodox Jewish boy, and Jesse Koochin (1998–2004), the son of religious Christians—parents have fought hospitals in court for the right to opt out of the brain-death standard in favor of the cardiopulmonary standards embraced by their own traditions. The family of Jahi McMath, a thirteen-year-old girl who was declared brain-dead after a surgical procedure in California in 2013 had their daughter relocated to New Jersey, one of two states that allow families to opt out of the brain-death standard on religious grounds. Her family removed her from life support in 2018, and a death certificate was issued.

The core question in these cases is whether a uniform measure of death is necessary, or whether flexibility should exist for those with sincerely held dissenting beliefs. Yet the matter is more complex: few families will be able to afford to pay to keep a brain-dead child on a ventilator indefinitely, so usually the public—through Medicaid or private insurance—will end up absorbing the costs. Death also has significant implications for the living: keeping a brain-dead person "alive" could prevent his heirs from inheriting in a timely manner, might continue alimony or social security indefinitely, and has implications for the ability of a surviving spouse to remarry without a divorce. Finally, one cannot ignore the fine line between divergent values and those that are truly macabre or gruesome. If a family wanted to take home the corpse of a loved one—a body dead by both cardiopulmonary and brain-death standards—with the plan of letting the cadaver decompose in its living room (let us say in a sealed, transparent bag to prevent the spread of disease), many people would object on the grounds that such an approach simply violates contemporary norms of decency. What is not clear is why the situation is different when that cadaver is hooked up to a machine.

72

Easing Suffering, Hastening Death

BABY FRANCES IS born with a severe terminal genetic disorder in which the skin and tissues form improperly. Her skin will eventually peel off, leaving the infant with wounds over large portions of her body. In all cases of the disorder, the baby's internal organs suffer the same fate and break down. No child has ever survived more than six months with this disease.

Doctors wish to give Baby Frances high doses of morphine to make certain that she is not in pain. However, the morphine needed to keep Baby Frances pain-free also reduces respiration rates and increases the chance of a premature death. The infant's parents, Eli and Delilah, vehemently object. They belong to a devout religious sect opposed to all forms of euthanasia. Victims of euthanasia and assisted suicide, they believe, will have to wait longer before their souls are permitted to enter heaven. For Eli and Delilah, giving morphine that may shorten the child's life, even if that is not the doctors' primary intention, is immoral. "We don't want our child to suffer," says Eli. "But we also want to make certain that there is a place for her in the afterlife."

Should the doctors try to obtain a court order to administer the analgesics over the parents' sincere religious objections?

REFLECTION: Pediatric Euthanasia

PARENTS ARE GENERALLY allowed to make medical decisions for their young children with the understanding that they will act in the children's best interests. In cases where the parents' sense of a child's interest differ from society's—such as Christian Scientists who oppose medication for severe but treatable illnesses—the state often imposes its own standards. However, a "best interest standard" becomes more challenging to enforce when the consensus of physicians is that an infant would be better off dying more quickly.

Several nations, including the Netherlands and Belgium, have decriminalized euthanasia for minors. In 2005, Dutch physician Eduard Verhagen proposed what has come to be known as the Groningen protocol, for ending the lives of infants experiencing hopeless and unbearable suffering. These children are usually given lethal combinations of the drugs morphine and midazolam. Crucial to the Groningen protocol is the consent of the child's parents. Parental consent may prove a practical necessity—by making the procedure politically palatable to those who might balk at terminating a sick child's life over the objections of her parents. Yet requiring parental consent to take such action differs from the criteria used regarding other medical interventions, from chemotherapy to surgery, where the best interests of the child are held paramount.

One justification for the distinction may be that losing a child is often a profoundly traumatic experience; since Eli and

Delilah will have to live with the consequences of Baby Frances's death—to a far greater degree than will her doctors—an ethical assessment of ending her life prematurely might also assess its impact on them. However, such an approach runs the risk of rolling down a slippery slope: Decisions to end life support for unconscious adults, for example, might similarly be assessed for their impact on the survivors, rather than solely upon the previously expressed wishes of the patients. Creating a "survivors veto" runs the risk of undermining patient autonomy.

In discussing cases like that of Baby Frances, ethicists often speak of the "dual effect" of giving morphine. The goal of the additional medication is pain control; death is merely an unintended, or unavoidable, secondary consequence. While this distinction may have philosophical merit, it is often of little solace to couples like Eli and Delilah.

73

Death and Taxes

CORNELIUS IS A ninety-two-year-old widowed banker with terminal heart failure. He is in a hospital, on a ventilator, and drifts in and out of consciousness, but even when conscious, he appears profoundly confused. His family visits regularly, and they appear deeply devoted to him. This has been his condition since early November.

As the end of the year approaches, Cornelius's family asks for a meeting with Dr. Benway, the head of the cardiology unit. The family explains that they want to take Cornelius off the ventilator. In the course of the meeting, their underlying motivation becomes clear. "He's going to die anyway," says his eldest son. "If not this month, then next month. But if he dies after January first, the tax code will have changed dramatically, and half of his fortune will go Uncle Sam rather than to his grandchildren. My father never would have wanted that." To Dr. Benway's surprise, the patient's other six children all agree that he would rather die sooner so as not to lose the tax advantage.

Is it ethical to turn off Cornelius's life support, which will likely lead to his rapid death, for the purposes of securing a tax break for his estate?

~~~

REFLECTION: Inheritance

SINCE MOST JURISDICTIONS expect family members—either as healthcare proxies or decision-making surrogates—to honor the end-of-life preferences of their loved ones, the first question to ask in this scenario is how the hospital should handle the situation if Cornelius were himself fully competent and making such a request. The assumption is often made that all patients who are suicidal or wish to end their own lives are mentally ill. This is not the case. Many patients want either to end their own lives actively or to withdraw medical care for highly rational reasons. These might be medical reasons—such as concern over pain, loss of dignity, or resignation to a terminal prognosis. Yet they may also transcend health-related matters. An elderly woman might prefer that money spent on nursing care be saved so that she can leave a legacy for her church or pay for her grandchildren's college educations. A utilitarian philosopher, plagued with a fatal disease, might not want to squander scarce healthcare resources. All states will honor a request from a mentally sound patient not suffering from a psychiatric condition to withdraw care—no matter what the underlying purpose or motive. Seven states (Oregon, Washington, California, Vermont, Montana, Hawaii, and Colorado) and the District of Columbia, under limited circumstances, allow patients to end their lives through active methods. That means that if Cornelius's mind is intact and he wants to turn off his life support to avoid paying estate taxes, doctors will have to honor his request. (Despite the well-known adage about the certainty of death and taxes, it seems even taxes can be avoided on occasion.)

This scenario is more complicated, as Cornelius is not able to make his own decisions. Rather, his children—as is often the case—have been called upon to render decisions for him. They clearly have a potential conflict of interest, though, in that they stand to inherit more money if their father dies within the calendar year. That fact alone does not change the standard for determining Cornelius's fate: Dr. Benway must do what the patient would have wanted. However, when such a possible competing motive exists, medical providers and courts may look for more convincing evidence to indicate that the family really is expressing the patient's wishes. Written documentation, conversations witnessed by third parties, or even the patient's overall life conduct may help clarify the appropriate decision in cases such as this. Under rare circumstances, a hospital ethics committee or a court (depending on the jurisdiction) may replace or overrule a proxy or surrogate who they do not believe is serving the patient's wishes honestly.

Cases like that of Cornelius appear not to be only hypothetical. A peculiarity of George W. Bush–era tax legislation was that the inheritance tax on wealthy Americans expired on December 31, 2009, and did not resume again until January 1, 2011. Rich folks who died in the interval saved vast sums of money. At that time, trusts-and-estates attorney Andrew Katzenstein told the *Wall Street Journal* that at least a dozen clients had inserted provisions into their healthcare-proxy forms allowing their proxies to make decisions based on the tax code. One client even inquired whether seeking euthanasia in the Netherlands, where physician-assisted suicide is legal, would qualify him for the tax break. According to Katzenstein, it would have.

74

"Did He Have AIDS?"

MONTY, A FIFTY-YEAR-OLD roofer who is positive for HIV, the virus that causes AIDS, has been treated by Dr. Kildare for many years, but often skips his prescribed HIV medications for months at a time. One summer afternoon, Monty becomes short of breath while working and is rushed to the nearest hospital with a collapsed lung—the result of a walking pneumonia that likely resulted from his untreated HIV/AIDS. Soon Monty loses consciousness and is placed on a ventilator; his prognosis for recovery is poor.

As Monty's condition deteriorates, Dr. Kildare contacts the patient's only immediate living relative, his sister, Crystal, to make decisions about Monty's medical care. In the past, Monty has told Dr. Kildare that he loves his sister very much but does not want her to know that he is HIV-positive or that he used to inject intravenous drugs, because such knowledge would upset her. By the time Crystal arrives at the hospital, Monty has already died. "I want to know what really killed my brother," Crystal says to Dr. Kildare. "For peace of mind. Healthy middle-aged men don't just drop dead of pneumonia. He didn't have HIV or AIDS, did he?" She demands to see Monty's medical records.

Should Dr. Kildare tell her that Monty had HIV, or should he make an effort to conceal this information by having it removed from Monty's medical records?

REFLECTION: **Posthumous Privacy**

PHYSICIANS HAVE LONG recognized that the ethical duty to preserve confidentiality should continue, at least to some degree, beyond the grave. Otherwise, many patients—especially those in the latter stages of life—might withhold critical, even life-prolonging information from their doctors. This principle is legally codified in the Health Insurance Portability and Accountability Act of 1996 (HIPAA), which initially ensured such confidentiality in perpetuity but has since been amended to shield patients' healthcare information for fifty years. Many state laws also protect posthumous medical confidentiality. However, one must distinguish between "confidentiality" and "privacy." While privacy rights entail the ability to keep information from *everyone*—such as material printed in a diary or shared with a priest—confidentiality protections permit disclosure to individuals who have a legitimate stake in accessing such information, including other physicians involved in the patient's care, healthcare insurers, and certain government agencies. In most jurisdictions, a patient's surviving agent—either his next of kin or his healthcare executor—generally acquires control of the patient's medical record. That control affords this agent the right to access the patient's healthcare information and to share it with others.

Allowing patients to keep medical information from survivors may help maximize their autonomy and sense of empowerment. Some critics might argue that Monty could have taken legal steps to prevent his sister from accessing his medical record entirely, such as appointing a third party to serve as his healthcare executor and then instructing that individual in writing not to share this information with Crystal. In many states, those actions would be both legally possible and binding. But requiring such drastic action may demand too much foresight from the average patient. More concerning, asking Monty to shut out Crystal entirely could undermine his ultimate goal—to protect her from unnecessary distress. The American Medical Association's Council on Ethical and Judicial Affairs urges doctors, to the extent possible, to preserve the same degree of confidentiality for patients in death as they have requested in life.

Of course, the logistics of concealing information from a determined relative may prove difficult. Would one remove Monty's medication list from the chart? Redact the name of the often AIDS-related bacteria that caused his pneumonia? Refusing Crystal access to the medical chart entirely would likely not be legal; even if it were legal, doing so might merely serve to provoke her worst suspicions, which certainly would not have been Monty's intent. Alternatively, Crystal might mistakenly conclude that her brother was healthy at baseline and thus died of substandard care—leading to a groundless malpractice suit.

An even more challenging situation arises when the patient

is critically ill but not yet deceased. In these cases, a family member—serving as a healthcare proxy or surrogate—often must render medical decisions on his behalf. Yet a decision maker needs accurate and comprehensive information about a patient's medical condition in order to generate informed choices. Under such conditions, when the patient's wishes regarding confidentiality directly conflict with his physical welfare, physicians may prove far less willing to withhold information, especially if the result is a surrogate or proxy making a poorly informed and dangerous decision.

75

Stranded on a Ventilator

A MAJOR HURRICANE strikes a midsize US city located on the southeast coast. The city's largest hospital, which is situated on a peninsula, loses electricity and cell phone service. It is entirely shut off from the outside world. Fierce winds batter the building, and after the storm abates, temperatures on the wards rise to over ninety degrees. Much of the staff abandons the hospital on makeshift rafts, leaving only Dr. Abigail Bartlet and a handful of nurses to care for more than twenty extremely ill intensive care unit (ICU) patients. Dr. Bartlet realizes that the backup generators will run out of energy after forty-eight hours, shutting off the machines that are keeping many of her patients alive.

One of the patients, Sylvia, is a quadriplegic woman who needs a ventilator to survive. She summons Dr. Bartlet and says to her, "You and I both know these machines are going to shut off eventually and I'm going to die a painful death. I'm seventy-two years old. I've lived a good life. What I want right now is a lethal dose of morphine so I can pass with comfort and dignity."

Physician-assisted suicide is illegal in this state. Although

Dr. Bartlet knows this, she fulfills Sylvia's request, and Sylvia dies. Two hours later, before the generators fail, the National Guard arrives to evacuate the remaining patients.

Has Dr. Bartlet acted ethically?

∼∾∼

REFLECTION: Physician-Assisted Suicide

SHOULD COMPETENT ADULTS should be allowed to end their own lives with physician assistance, and, if so, under what circumstances? Jurisdictions permitting "aid in dying" in the United States generally confine the practice to the terminally ill and require consistent, repeated requests over a period of time. However, doctors are allowed to prescribe medications that shorten life if their primary purpose is to relieve pain or suffering. This exception is known as the "double effect doctrine." In Dr. Bartlet's state, physician-assisted suicide is illegal; she may well face criminal charges. A key question for the courts would be whether she intended to kill Sylvia—or, rather, to sedate her with the morphine to alleviate her discomfort until help could arrive. From the standpoint of ethical analysis, one might also ask whether Sylvia could really have made an autonomous, fully informed decision in the context of an isolated, storm-ravaged hospital.

The second question raised by this scenario is to what degree emergency circumstances, such as mass-casualty events, allow for exceptions to the general rules of medical conduct.

Historically, some ethical codes have embraced the "doctrine of necessity"—the argument that an otherwise unacceptable action was justified to prevent a greater crime or moral offense. Survivors of shipwrecks who resorted to murder and cannibalism—like those from the whaleship *Essex* (1820), which inspired *Moby-Dick*, and the French yacht *Mignonette* (1884)—often justified their actions on these grounds. However, no consensus exists among ethicists as to whether necessity can be used to justify assisted suicide to prevent suffering during a catastrophic event. During the aftermath of Hurricane Katrina, the staff at New Orleans's Memorial Medical Center, under the direction of physician Anna Pou, allegedly injected lethal cocktails into patients who could not be evacuated. Colleagues defended Pou, a highly regarded clinician, who insisted the medication was aimed at relieving pain and suffering. She was later charged with murder, but a grand jury declined to indict her, and she has since played a role in rewriting Louisiana law to provide medical personal with civil immunity for such conduct during emergencies. Journalist Sheri Fink, who has been critical of the choices made at Memorial, won the Pulitzer Prize for her coverage of the episode, later expanded into the 2013 book *Five Days at Memorial: Life and Death in a Storm-Ravaged Hospital*.

Medical writer Amanda Schaffer observed in the *New Yorker* that "medical workers under siege can easily lose perspective. They can start to make decisions based on their own dark fears rather than the changing facts on the ground." One way to avoid this seemingly inevitable problem might be to establish clear rules in advance for medical conduct during large-scale disasters. However, physicians might still violate such rules when confronting extreme circumstances if they believe doing so reflects the ethical course of action.

76

"Give Me My Late Fiancé's Sperm"

FELIX AND SADIE are engaged to be married when Felix falls down the elevator shaft of his building and is critically injured. The doctors inform Sadie, along with Felix's only living close relative, Uncle Rufus, that he will not survive.

Sadie and Felix had planned to have a baby shortly after their marriage. Having seen a television show in which sperm is harvested from a dying man to inseminate his spouse, Sadie asks whether this is possible for her. Uncle Rufus adamantly objects. "Felix wanted a baby, sure," he says. "But a baby *the natural way*. With a father. He would never have agreed to father a child after he died." It is worth noting that, since Felix and Sadie were not yet married, Uncle Rufus is the only heir to Felix's estate, which includes a sizable inheritance from his late parents.

Should the doctors agree to harvest Felix's sperm in order to impregnate Sadie over Uncle Rufus's protestations?

REFLECTION: Posthumous Sperm Retrieval

POSTHUMOUS SPERM RETRIEVAL (PSR) has been available in the United States since 1978, when urologist Cappy M. Rothman initially performed the procedure. The first successful childbirth from the intervention occurred in 1999. Sperm generally has to be harvested within thirty-six hours of death, requiring rapid decision-making on the part of surviving partners and relatives. While the procedure is biologically feasible, it remains ethically controversial.

Critics of PSR object on the grounds that individuals, even if deceased, should not become parents in the absence of their own consent. According to Orthodox Jewish custom, which forbids the practice, PSR violates the ban on using a cadaver for personal interest. Opponents also raise concerns about the welfare of the future children. Supporters note that many men father offspring without wishing to do so, through casual or careless sexual practices, and that many children are raised successfully by single parents.

Some Western nations, including France and Germany, prohibit PSR. In the United States, PSR is legal, but physicians still reject many cases. Peter N. Schlegel, a prominent New York City urologist, told the *New York Times* in 2004 that he uses a "prudential conservative approach" that led him to refuse eighteen of twenty-two requests. Courts often apply "substituted judgment" in determining whether to allow partners to harvest sperm, asking if the deceased man would have wanted to father children posthumously. Some demand evidence of prior consent—such as a conversation on the subject. Others are willing to accept "implied consent" revealed by evidence of an active effort to conceive children. Generally, only partners—whether married or not—are permitted to authorize sperm extractions. Yet in 2009, a Texas judge allowed Marissa Evans to harvest sperm from her murdered son, Nikolas, with the intent of hiring a surrogate to give birth to a future grandchild. In a parallel case, a fifty-nine-year-old British woman—identified only as Mrs. M—fought (ultimately without success) to be impregnated with embryos frozen by her deceased daughter.

In Felix's case, Uncle Rufus may have the better part of the argument unless Sadie can offer persuasive evidence that Felix would have wanted to have children under these circumstances. Many states regard Uncle Rufus, as Felix's only relative, to be his surrogate for medical decision-making. (Yet laws do vary; some states recognize a domestic partner or even a close friend, while in others an uncle is too distantly related to qualify.) In order to prevail in court, Sadie would likely have to convince a judge that Uncle Rufus—possibly motivated by avarice—is flouting Felix's hypothetical wishes. Under circumstances where the patient's wishes are doubtful and the survivors stand in discord, few medical authorities are likely to advocate for the procedure.

77

Waiting For Reincarnation

ALEXANDER IS A forty-nine-year-old man who comes to a prominent teaching hospital for a heart transplant. While awaiting the transplant, he is placed on a machine called a BIVAD, or biventricular assist device—basically, an artificial heart the size of a small refrigerator to tide him over until a donor heart becomes available. While awaiting a heart, he suffers a severe stroke.

The doctors tell his wife, Katie, that no patient who has suffered such a severe stroke has ever regained consciousness and that Alexander is no longer a candidate for transplant. They would like to turn off the BIVAD and allow nature to take its course. Not lost upon these doctors is that Alexander occupies a desperately needed ICU bed, which could benefit other patients, and that his care costs the healthcare system upwards of $10,000 a day. They are also aware than Alexander could survive for years on the BIVAD and the other machines that are now helping to keep him alive: a ventilator and a dialysis machine.

Katie refuses to yield to the doctors' request. "I realize he has no chance of recovery," she says. "But Alexander believed deeply in reincarnation. What mattered most to him was that he die at the right moment—so that his soul could return to Earth in the body for which it was destined. To him, that would have meant keeping him on the machines until all brain function ceases, even if it means decades. I feel obligated to honor those wishes."

Should the doctors go to court to overrule Katie's decision?

REFLECTION: Death-Defying Decisions

FROM THE 1970s to the 1990s, most end-of-life conflicts between families and hospitals involved cases where the family wanted to withdraw life support and the medical facility objected. These families often fought public battles through the court system in the hopes of letting their loved ones die "naturally." Over the past two decades, the disagreements between families and providers have increasingly been reversed: in a series of high-profile disputes, hospitals have sought to withdraw life support in cases of supposed medical futility, while families have fought to keep their loved ones on ventilators. Among the earliest and best-known of these cases was that of Helga Wanglie, an eighty-six-year-old Minnesota woman in a persistent vegetative state whose doctors wanted to withdraw care over her husband's objections. (A court ultimately ruled for her family, but she died anyway two days later.) In 2005, ethicist Lachlan Forrow of Boston's Beth Israel Deaconess Medical Center told the *New York Times*: "About 15 years ago, at least 80 percent of the cases were right-to-die kinds of cases. Today, it's more like at least 80 percent of the cases are the other direction: family members who are pushing for continued or more aggressive life support and doctors and nurses who think that that's wrong." These cases can prove extremely costly for the healthcare system. Helga Wanglie's final years of medical care, for instance, reportedly carried a price tag of $800,000 in 1991 dollars—or about $1.5 million today.

The motives for keeping patients on life support past the point of "futility" vary greatly. Some families hold out hope, often irrationally, that their relatives will recover. Yet the media intermittently reports precisely those sorts of miraculous tales: On the day that the family of fifty-six-year-old Nebraska mother Teri Roberts planned to turn off her ventilator in 2015, the toxic shock syndrome patient awoke from her "irreversible" coma. Car crash victim Terry Wallis woke up in 2003 after nearly two decades. Canadian woman Annie Shapiro fell into a coma on the day John F. Kennedy was assassinated in 1963—and woke up suddenly in 1992! Other families recognize that their relatives will not improve but have religious or cultural reasons for refusing to terminate care, as in Alexander's case; his prognosis for recovery is not relevant to his wife's decision-making process.

State laws vary on whether hospitals can ever overrule families in these cases. Texas affords providers the greatest power in the area. Under the Texas Advance Directives Act of 2009 (better known as the Texas Futile Care Law), hospitals can withdraw life support from patients when such care is deemed "futile," once certain procedural safeguards are met. Among the first patients affected by the law were infant Sun Hudson and terminal cancer patient Tirhas Habtegiris.

Scenarios like the conflict between Alexander's wife and his physicians can often be prevented. Had the hospital's medical team discussed with the couple in advance the precise circumstances under which life support would be withdrawn, and emphasized the societal costs of keeping patients with no prognosis of recovery on life support, it is always possibly that Alexander might have accepted these terms; alternatively, the hospital might not have offered him the BIVAD at all. Like many cases in medical ethics, these issues are best addressed before the fact—rather than after tragedy strikes.

78

Cadaver Confusion

THE MORGUE AT a community hospital serves the anatomy lab at a nearby medical school. Each year, dozens of dying patients at the hospital—often retired physicians and nurses—agree to donate their bodies for dissection by first-year medical students.

Dr. Scarpetta, the chief pathologist, goes on maternity leave. She leaves her assistant, Dr. Minoret, in charge of the morgue while she is gone. When she returns, she reviews Dr. Minoret's work and discovers that a terrible error has occurred: the corpse of one patient ("Jed"), which was supposed to be sent to the family for cremation, was actually sent to the anatomy lab for dissection, while a corpse donated to the lab ("Bud") was instead released to a funeral home. The error occurred over three months earlier, and Jeb's body has already been embalmed in formaldehyde and dissected by medical students. Bud's body has presumably been cremated. Dr. Scarpetta fears that revealing the morgue's mistake, which is now irreversible, will cause the surviving family members unnecessary and possibly extreme distress. In contrast, if she conceals the mistake—and alters the records—there is no way they will ever know.

Should Dr. Scarpetta inform the next of kin of the error?

REFLECTION: Therapeutic Privilege

CORPSES ARE SENT to the wrong families frequently—at least, if one believes the media hype. For sensationalism, what can beat headlines like the *Sacramento Bee*'s cry, BABY'S CORPSE MISTAKENLY BURIED WITH TWINS (2006). While assessing the actual incidence of such mix-ups is nigh impossible, since many likely go undiscovered, the reactions of survivors generally reflect varying degrees of outrage. A lawyer for the family of Billie Sue Smith of Tennessee, who was inadvertently buried in the grave of a man named John Hughes, summed up these frustrations as follows: "You know the adage, 'May she rest in peace'? Well, there's no peace here. To know you have ashes of the cremains of a loved one that may not be their ashes? To visit the grave of a loved one and the loved one may not be in that grave? There's no peace." The harm done in these cases is generally considered to be psychological, rather than economically or physically tangible. Followers of some religious traditions may believe otherwise, however, if they relate the fate of a corpse to their loved one's future in the afterlife. Yet widespread social customs relating to respect for the dead suggest that most victims of such a mishap will experience distress.

"Therapeutic privilege" refers to the process of withholding information from a patient or patient's family member because sharing the information is either medically contraindicated or would cause the patient great harm with no benefit. It is an example of medical paternalism—once the dominant principle in medical practice. Over the past half century, Western medicine has rejected such paternalism as the default standard in healthcare in favor of patient autonomy. Yet there may be extreme cases where withholding information—at least for a period of time—would prove justified. Examples might include not informing an accident victim of the extent of her injuries for a few hours until appropriate family support can be obtained, or withholding a diagnosis that might put a severely depressed patient at risk of suicide. The American Medical Association looks highly unfavorably upon the practice, barring extraordinary circumstances. Its Code of Medical Ethics states, "Withholding medical information from patients without their knowledge or consent is ethically unacceptable."

In theory, the tragic mistake in Dr. Scarpetta's lab might justify withholding information from Bud's and Jed's families as an extension of the therapeutic-privilege principle on the grounds that the revelation would likely cause considerable psychological damage and would be unlikely to provide any benefit. If the mistake were truly undiscoverable in the future and psychological distress probable, utilitarian ethicists would argue against disclosure on the grounds that it would do more harm than good.

One should note the difference in this case from one where babies are mistakenly exchanged at birth and the mishap is later discovered. In that situation, withholding the error has considerable practical effects on the victims. They will not know their correct medical histories and may fail to connect with their "adoptive" families. In contrast, no practical harm results from visiting the wrong grave. All the tangible damage in the case of Bud and Jed—such as the cremation and embalming, which have undermined the late men's wishes—has already been done. Yet juries are likely to compensate families for the distress caused by such lapses. That may prove to be the most concrete benefit of disclosure at a societal level: if the hospital is forced to compensate the families in this case, Dr. Scarpetta will take considerably greater care in the future when allocating work while away. In the long run, such settlements may serve as powerful deterrents, reducing the likelihood of additional morgue mishaps.

79

"He'd Rather Die Than Live Like This"

CLARENCE IS A fifty-year-old outdoorsman who loves fishing, hunting, and horseback riding, but his deepest passion is for wood carving. He works as a carpenter. One summer, while camping in the wilderness, he contracts a bacterial infection and must be airlifted to a community hospital. By the time he arrives, his blood pressure had dropped so low that he had lost consciousness; blood perfusion to his hands and feet has been minimal for hours. The doctors have grim news for his sisters, Edna and Ethel, who are his only immediate relatives. Even with aggressive antibiotic treatment, which may yet save his life, his hands and feet will have to be amputated.

Edna says, "I guess that's our only choice. Clarence is a fighter. He would have wanted to live at all costs." Ethel disagrees. "Our brother would never want to live so disabled," she says. "The outdoors and physical labor are his life. You have to stop these aggressive antibiotics, doctor. Let nature take its course. I wouldn't want him to suffer the torture of waking up in this state." According to the doctors, if the antibiotics work and Clarence ultimately regains consciousness but is unwilling to live in his new condition, there will be nothing they can legally do to help him end his life.

Should the doctors continue with the aggressive antibiotic treatment or stop it and let Clarence die?

REFLECTION: Withdrawing Life Support

QUESTIONS SURROUNDING WHEN to halt aggressive care and to remove life support did not surface frequently in medicine until the 1970s, when new technologies—from ventilators and dialysis machines to more powerful antihypotensive agents and antibiotics—made it possible to prolong the lives of the critically ill as never before. Right-to-die cases that entered the public discourse, such as those of Karen Ann Quinlan (1954–1985) and Nancy Cruzan (1957–1990), resulted as much from improved medical care as from any change in ethical norms.

Clarence's case raises two distinct issues that often arise in contemporary medical ethics: how to weigh "sanctity of life" against "quality of life" and what to do when an incapacitated patient's wishes are unclear and family members cannot agree.

Advocates for upholding the sanctity of life believe that human life has intrinsic value and should be preserved at all costs. Historically, many religious conservatives have adopted this position. In contrast, critics of this standard argue that, under some circumstances, the quality of a person's life drops so low that aggressive care or life support no longer makes sense. At their extremes, both positions prove highly controversial.

Utilitarian philosopher Peter Singer, a strong champion of the quality-of-life position, has used it to justify euthanasia for disabled infants. The entire nation saw the extremes that sanctity-of-life advocates adopted to keep Terri Schiavo alive in 2005 over the objections of her husband and her own reported wishes.

One should note that under ordinary circumstances, these two values are not in conflict: doctors are usually laboring *both* to prolong a patient's life and to improve its quality. Ethicist Dan Callahan has noted that there is an imbalance between these two standards: "sanctity of life" leads to minimal ambiguity, while the minimum quality of life one might be willing to tolerate varies greatly from person to person. Advance directives, such as living wills and healthcare proxies, which spell out one's wishes long in advance of illness, are designed to address this subjectivity. Yet such documents raise the question of whether a healthy person can predict with accuracy what she would want if she became critically ill, without having already experienced such an illness. Patients are frequently known to "bargain down": to adjust their standards to accept a lower quality of life than they would have when healthy, once they actually find themselves in a more impaired condition.

The purpose of appointing a healthcare proxy is to empower an agent to act on one's behalf if a person can no longer make medical decisions. Healthy people are advised to discuss their end-of-life wishes with their proxies. In the absence of a proxy, nearly every state enables a so-called "surrogate," often a closely related family member, to make decisions for the patient. State laws provide for hierarchies of surrogates: usually, spouses take precedence over adult children, followed by parents, siblings, collateral relatives, and sometimes even close friends. When two or more surrogates of equal rank cannot agree—as with Clarence's sisters—states vary widely in how to resolve the disagreement. Some, like New York and Maryland, refer the case to a committee of experts to address the matter, which may ultimately end up decided in court, while West Virginia lets the doctors choose which surrogate has the stronger claim based on such factors as perceived knowledge of the patient and degree of concern. In cases with an odd number of potential decision makers, some states allow for a majority vote.

The challenge of cases like Clarence's is that nobody can predict whether he will thrive or suffer in his new condition. A closely related set of cases involve patients who wake up on ventilators after enduring C2 level spinal cord injuries that render them lifelong quadriplegics who will remain permanently dependent on machines to breathe. When these patients awake from medically induced comas or sedation, they often demand (via computerized eye trackers) that their ventilators be shut off, insisting they would rather die than live in their impaired conditions. In these cases, the patient *is* expressing a clear wish—but one that may be compromised by shock or depression. One of the most contentious disagreements in many hospitals surrounds how long such patients should be compelled to remain on life support over their objections, often suffering existentially during this time, while psychiatrists and therapists attempt to help them adjust to their new lives.

Some patients in Clarence's condition go on to thrive. British newspapers have reported on the case of John Middleton, who lost four limbs at age forty-four due to flesh-eating bacteria—but managed to regain a fulfilling life with the help of prosthetics and a supportive partner. At the same time, the media rarely reports on quadruple amputees who lead lives of silent desperation in institutions, wishing their providers or relatives had withdrawn care when they had an opportunity to do so.

FURTHER READING

Reflection #1

Anderson, Kermyt G. "How Well Does Paternity Confidence Match Actual Paternity? Evidence from Worldwide Nonpaternity Rates." *Current Anthropology* 47, no. 3 (June 2006).

Lerner, Barron H. "Cases; When a Doctor Stumbles on a Family Secret." *New York Times*, September 16, 2003.

Reflection #2

Faden, Ruth R., Tom L. Beauchamp, and Nancy M. P. King. *A History and Theory of Informed Consent*. New York: Oxford University Press, 1986.

Mariner, Wendy K., and George J. Annas. "Informed Consent and the First Amendment," *New England Journal of Medicine* 372, no. 14 (April 2, 2015): 1285–87.

Rothman D. J. "The Shame of Medical Research," *New York Review of Books*, March 8, 2001.

Reflection #3

Appelbaum, Paul S., and Alan Meisel. "Therapists' Obligations to Report Their Patients' Criminal Acts," *Bulletin of the American Academy of Psychiatry and the Law* 14, no.3 (February 1986): 221–30.

Goldman, Marcus J., and Thomas G. Gutheil. "The Misperceived Duty to Report Patients' Past Crimes." *Bulletin of the American Academy of Psychiatry and the Law* 22, no. 3 (September 1994): 407–10.

Jaffee v. Redmond, 518 U.S. 1 (1996).

Tarasoff v. Regents of the University of California, 17 Cal. 3d 425 (1976).

Reflection #4

Accordino, Robert, Nicholas Kopple-Perry, Nada Gligorov, and Stephen Krieger. "The Medical Record as Legal Document: When Can the Patient Dictate the Content?" *Clinical Ethics* 9, no. 1 (January 7, 2014): 53–56.

Golodetz, A., J. Ruess, and R. L. Milhous. "The Right to Know: Giving the Patient His Medical Record." *Archives of Physical Medicine and Rehabilitation* 57, no. 2 (February 1976):78–81.

Steiner, P. "Patient Access to the Medical Record: A Study of Physician Attitudes." *Medical Record News* 49, no. 4 (August 1978): 77–78, 80–81.

Reflection #5

Altman, Lawrence K., and Todd S. Purdum. "In J.F.K. File, Hidden Illness, Pain and Pills." *New York Times*, November 17, 2002.

Appel, Jacob M. "History's DNA." *Chicago Tribune*, August 21, 2008.

Brown, David. "Is Lincoln Earliest Recorded Case of Rare Disease?" *Washington Post*, November 26, 2007.

Davidson, Jonathan, Kathryn Connor, and Marvin S. Swartz. "Mental Illness in U.S. Presidents Between 1776 and 1974: A Review of Biographical Sources." *Journal of Nervous and Mental Disease* 194, no. 1 (January 2006): 47–51.

Ferrell, R. H. *Ill-Advised: Presidential Health and Public Trust*, 53–150. Columbia, MO: University of Missouri Press, 1996.

Gugliotta, Guy. "DNA May Reveal Who Can Claim Columbus," *Washington Post*, May 15, 2006

Hazelgrove, William. *Madam President: The Secret Presidency of Edith Wilson*. Washington, DC: Regnery, 2016

Sotos, John G. *The Physical Lincoln Complete*. Mt. Vernon, VA: Mt. Vernon Book Systems, 2008.

Watson, Robert P., and Dale Berger. "Reconsidering Ike's Health and Legacy: A Surprising Lesson in Duty at the Little White House Residential Retreat." Eisenhower Institute.

Reflection #6

Payton v. Weaver, Cal. Ct. App., 182 Cal. Rptr. 225 (1982).

Sack, Kevin. "Hospital Falters as Refuge for Illegal Immigrants." *New York Times*, November 20, 2009.

Reflection #7

English, Peter C., and Herman Grossman. "Radiology and the History of Child Abuse," *Pediatric Annals* 12, no. 12 (December 1983): 870–74.

Kempe, C. Henry, Frederic N. Silverman, Brandt F. Steele, William Droegemueller, and Henry K. Silver. "The Battered-Child Syndrome." *JAMA* 181, no. 1 (1962):17–24.

Knight, Bernard "The History of Child Abuse," *Forensic Science International* 30, no. 2–3 (February–March 1986): 135–41.

Kotz, Deborah. "When Does Physical Discipline Become Child Abuse?" *Boston Globe*, September 17, 2014.

Reflection #8

Appel Jacob M. "May Physicians Date Their Patients' Relatives? Rethinking Sexual Misconduct & Disclosure after Long v. Ostroff." *Medicine and Health Rhode Island* 87, no. 5 (May 2004):159–61.

Chesler, Phyllis. "The Sensuous Psychiatrists," *New York*, June 19, 1972.

Freeman, Lucy, and Julie Roy. *Betrayal: The True Story of the First Woman to Successfully Sue Her Psychiatrist for Using Sex in the Guise of Therapy.* New York: Stein and Day, 1976.

Gartrell, N., J. Herman, S. Olarte, M. Feldstein, and R. Localio. "Psychiatrist-Patient Sexual Contact: Results of a National Survey. I: Prevalence." *American Journal of Psychiatry* 143, no. 9 (September 1986): 1126–31.

Reflection #9

Altman, Lawrence K. "When a Murderer Wants to Practice Medicine." *New York Times*, January 29, 2008.

Appel, Jacob M. "Sweden Asks: Should Convicted Murderers Practice Medicine?" *Cambridge Quarterly of Healthcare Ethics* 19, no. 4 (October 2010): 559–62.

Kmietovicz, Zosia. "R.E.S.P.E.C.T. Why Doctors Are Still Getting Enough of It." *BMJ* 324, no. 7328 (January 5, 2002): 11.

Rakatansky, Herbert. "Criminal Convictions and Medical Licensure." *AMA Journal of Ethics* 13, no. 10 (October 2011): 712–17.

Reflection #10

Beck, Julie. "'Do No Harm': When Doctors Torture." *Atlantic*, December 2014.

Jesper, S. "Doctors' Involvement in Torture." *Torture* 18, no. 3 (2008):161–75.

Singh, Jerome Amir. "American Physicians and Dual Loyalty Obligations in the 'War on Terror.'" *BMC Medical Ethics* 4, no. 1 (August 1, 2003): E4.

Reflection #11

Creswell, Julie, and Jessica Silver-Greenberg. "Dimon's Cancer and the Fine Line in Revealing Illness of a C.E.O." *New York Times*, July 2, 2014.

Horwich, Allan. "When the Corporate Luminary Becomes Seriously Ill: When Is a Corporation Obligated to Disclose That Illness and Should the Securities and Exchange Commission Adopt a Rule Requiring Disclosure?" *New York University Journal of Law and Business* 5, no. 2 (2009.)

Parloff, Roger. "Why the SEC Is Probing Steve Jobs: Behind the Investigation into the Timing of Disclosure of the Apple's Chief's Health Problems." *Fortune*, January 22, 2009.

Reflection #12

Ojanuga, D. "The Medical Ethics of the 'Father of Gynaecology,' Dr. J. Marion Sims." *Journal of Medical Ethics* 19, no. 1 (March 1993): 28–31.

Perry, Susan. "Nazi Link Isn't the Only Reason to Abandon Eponymous Medical Names." *Minnesota Post*, May 19, 2011.

Washington, Harriet A. *Medical Apartheid: The Dark History of Medical Experimentation on Black Americans from Colonial Times to the Present*. New York: Anchor, 2008.

Reflection #13

Costandi, Mo. "The Science and Ethics of Voluntary Amputation." *Guardian*, May 30, 2012.

Elliott, Carl. "A New Way to Be Mad," *Atlantic*, December 2000.

Kloster, Ulla. "I Live like a Disabled Person Even Though I'm Physically Healthy . . ." *Mail on Sunday*, July 16, 2013.

Reflection #14

Allen, David B., Michael Kappy, Douglas Diekema, and Norman Fost. "Growth-Attenuation Therapy: Principles for Practice." *Pediatrics* 123, no. 6 (June 2009): 1556–61.

Burkholder, Amy. "Disabled Girl's Parents Defend Growth-Stunting Treatment." CNN.com, March 12, 2008.

Davies, Caroline. "Ashley the Pillow Angel: Love or Madness?" *Telegraph*, January 5, 2007.

Gibbs, Nancy. "Pillow Angel Ethics." *Time*, January 7, 2007.

McDonald, Anne. "The Other Story from a 'Pillow Angel.'" SeattlePI.com, June 16, 2007.

Ostrom, Carol. "Child's Hysterectomy Illegal, Hospital Agrees." *Seattle Times*, May 9, 2007.

Pilkington, Ed. "The Ashley Treatment: 'Her Life Is As Good As We Can Possibly Make It.'" *Guardian*, March 15, 2012.

Reflection #15

Corbett, Sara. "A Cutting Tradition." *New York Times Magazine*, January 20, 2008

Westcott, Lucy. "Female Genital Mutilation on the Rise in the U.S." *Newsweek*, February 6, 2015.

Reflection #16

Kowalczyk, Liz. "Donor's Death Shatters Family, Stuns Surgeons." *Boston Globe*, February 2, 2014.

Miller, C. M., M.L. Smith, and Uso T. Diago. "Living Donor Liver Transplantation: Ethical Considerations." *Mount Sinai Journal of Medicine* 79, no. 2 (March–April 2012):214–22.

Reflection #17

"Anemia Victim McFall Dies of Hemorrhage." *Michigan Daily*, August 11, 1978.

McFall v. Shimp, 10 Pa. D. & C. 3d 90 (1978).

Wilkerson, Isabel. "In Marrow Donor Lawsuit, Altruism Collides With Right to Protect Child." *New York Times*, July 30, 1990.

Reflection #18

Flannery, Mary. "Stage of Illness Decides Priority But Some Docs Say There's Favoritism." *Daily News*, June 9, 1995.

Grady, Denise, and Barry Meier. "A Transplant That Is Raising Many Questions." *New York Times*, June 23, 2009.

Munson, Ronald. *Raising the Dead: Organ Transplants, Ethics, and Society*. New York: Oxford University Press, 2002.

Reflection #19

Appel, Jacob M., and Mark D. Fox. "Organ Solicitation on the Internet: Every Man for Himself?" *Hastings Center Report* 35, no. 3 (May–June 2005): 14.

Caplan, Arthur, Sheldon Zink, and Stacey Wertlieb. "Jumping to the Front of the Line for an Organ Transplant Is Unfair." *Chicago Tribune*, September 1, 2004.

Grantham, Dulcinea A. "Transforming Transplantation: The Effect of the Health and Human Services Final Rule on the Organ Allocation System." *University of San Francscio Law Rveview* 35 (Summer 2001); 751–52 .

Goldberg, Aviva. "Advertising for Organs." *AMA Journal of Ethics* 7, no. 9 (September 2005).: 619–24.

Roen, Terry O. "'Kindred Spirit' Donates a Kidney." *Orlando Sentinel*, August 13, 2005.

Reflection #20

Appel, Jacob M. "Wanted Dead or Alive? Kidney Transplantation in Inmates Awaiting Execution," *Journal of Clinical Ethics* 16, no. 1(Spring 2005): 58–60.

Lin, Shu S., Lauren Rich, Jay D. Pal, and Robert M. Sade. "Prisoners on Death Row Should Be Accepted as Organ Donors." *Annals of Thoracic Surgery* 93, no. 6 (June 2012): 1773–79.

Longo, Christian. "Giving Life after Death Row." *New York Times*, March 5, 2011.

Reflection #21

Armstrong, Scott. "'Baby Fae' Case Raises Tough Issues." *Christian Science Monitor*, November 6, 1984.

Cooper, David K. C. "A Brief History of Cross-Species Organ Transplantation." *Proceedings of Baylor University Medical Center* 25, no. 1 (January 2012): 49–57.

Hoke, Franklin. "Undaunted By Death of First Baboon Liver Recipient, Interdisciplinary Transplant Team Looks to the Future," *The Scientist*, September 28, 1992.

Krauthammer, Charles. "Essay: The Using of Baby Fae." *Time*, December 3, 1984.

Reflection #22

Caplan, Arthur. "Doctor Seeking to Perform Head Transplant Is Out of His Mind." *Forbes*, February 26, 2015.

McKie, Robin, and Nick Paton Walsh. "Trickster Has Transplant Hand Cut Off." *Guardian*, February 3, 2001.

Novak, Walter. "The Frankenstein Factor: Cleveland Brain Surgeon Robert J. White Has a Head for Transplanting." CleveScene.com, December 9, 1999.

Sample, Ian. "First Full Body Transplant Is Two Years Away, Surgeon Claims." *Guardian*, February 25, 2015.

Reflection #23

Gavin, Gabriel C. S.. "Should We Be Castrating Sex Offenders?" *Psychology Today*, October 6, 2014

Rondeaux, Candace. "Can Castration Be a Solution for Sex Offenders?" *Washington Post*, July 5, 2006.

Sealey, Geraldine. "Some Sex Offenders Opt for Castration," ABCNews.com, March 2, 2001.

Wassersug, R. J., S. A. Zelenietz, and G. F. Squire. "New Age Eunuchs: Motivation and Rationale for Voluntary Castration." *Archives of Sexual Behavior* 33, no. 5 (October 2004): 433–42.

Weinberger, Linda E., Shoba Sreenivasan, Thomas Garrick, and Hadley Osran. "The Impact of Surgical Castration on Sexual Recidivism Risk among Sexually Violent Predatory Offenders." *Journal of the American Academy of Psychiatry and the Law* 33, no. 1 (2005): 16–36.

Reflection #24

Appel, Jacob M. "In Defense of Tongue Splitting." *Journal of Clinical Ethics* 16, no. 3 (Fall 2005): 236–38.

Kennett, Heather. "Doctors Issue Warning on Body Modifications." *Sunday Mail*, July 2, 2011.

Patterson, J. "Tongue Splitting, a Bizarre Form of Body Piercing, Soon Will Be Illegal in Illinois." *Daily Herald*, August 7, 2003.

Reflection #25

Arnold, Wayne, and Denise Grady. "Twins Die Trying to Live Two Lives." *New York Times*, July 9, 2003.

Pearn, John. "Bioethical Issues in Caring for Conjoined Twins and Their Parents." *Lancet* 357, no. 9272 (June 16, 2001): 1968–71.

Reflection #26

Belkin, Lisa. "The Made-to-Order Savior." *New York Times Magazine*, July 1, 2001.

Levin, Angela. "I Know I Was Born to Save Charlie instead of Being Born Just for Me: Incredible Story of the Saviour Sibling Who Sparked an Ethical Furore." *Daily Mail*, May 21, 2011.

Sheldon S., and S. Wilkinson. "Should Selecting Saviour Siblings Be Banned?" *Journal of Medical Ethics* 30, no. 6 (2004): 533–37

Spriggs, M., and J. Savulescu. "'Saviour Siblings.'" *Journal of Medical Ethics* 28, no. 5 (October 2002): 289.

Verlinsky, Yury, S. Rechitsky, W. Schoolcraft, C. Strom, and A. Kulley. "Preimplantation Diagnosis for Fanconi Anemia Combined with HLA Matching." *JAMA* 285, no. 24 (June 27, 2001): 3130–33.

Reflection #27

Lawson, Dominic. "Of Course a Deaf Couple Want a Deaf Child." *Independent*, March 11, 2008.

Porter, Gerard, and Malcolm K. Smith. "Preventing the Selection of 'Deaf Embryos' under the Human Fertilisation and Embryology Act 2008: Problematizing Disability?" *New Genetics and Society* 32, no. 2 (2013).

Starr, Sandy. "Should We Stamp Out 'Designer Deafness'?" *Spiked*, March 31, 2008.

Reflection #28

Forster, Heidi. "Law and Ethics Meet: When Couples Fight Over Their Frozen Embryos." *Journal of Andrology* 21, no. 4 (July–August 2000): 512–14.

Loeb, Nick. "Sofía Vergara's Ex-Fiancé: Our Frozen Embryos Have a Right to Live." *New York Times*, April 29, 2015.

Young, Natalie K. "Frozen Embryos: New Technology Meets Family Law." *Golden Gate University Law Review* 21, no. 3 (January 1991).

Reflection #29

Marrus, Ellen. (2002). "Crack Babies and the Constitution: Ruminations about Addicted Pregnant Women after Ferguson v. City of Charleston." *Villanova Law Review* 47, no. 2 (2002): 299–340.

Rhode, Deborah L. "The Terrible War on Pregnant Drug Users." *New Republic*, July 17, 2014.

Ronan, Alex. "Here's What Happens When Pregnant Women Lose Their Rights." *New York*, April 2, 2015.

Reflection #30

Bower, Hedy R. "How Far Can a State Go to Protect a Fetus? The Rebecca Comeau Story and the Case for Requiring Massachusetts to Follow the U.S. Constitution." *Golden Gate University Law Review* 31, no. 2 (2001).

Cherry, April L. "The Detention, Confinement, and Incarceration of Pregnant Women for the Benefit of Fetal Health." *Columbia Journal of Gender & Law* 16, no. 147 (2007).

Nicolosi, Michele. "Forced Prenatal Care." *Salon*, September 15, 2000.

Reflection 31

Belluck, Pam. "The Right to Be a Father (or Not)." *New York Times*, November 6, 2005.

Cohen, I. Glenn. "The Constitution and the Rights Not to Procreate." *Stanford Law Review* 60, no. 4 (April 2010): 1135.

McCulley, Melanie G. "The Male Abortion: The Putative Father's Right to Terminate His Interests in and Obligations to the Unborn Child." *Journal of Law and Policy* 7, no. 1 (1988)1–55.

Planned Parenthood of Southeastern Pennsylvania v. Casey, 505 U.S. 833 (1992).

Young, Cathy. "A Man's Right to Choose." *Salon*, October 19, 2000.

Reflection #32

Hartocollis, Anemona. "Mother Accuses Doctors of Forcing a C-Section and Files Suit." *New York Times*, May 16, 2014.

Levy, Daniel R. "The Maternal-Fetal Conflict: The Right of a Woman to Refuse a Cesarean Section versus the State's Interest in Saving the Life of the Fetus." *West Virginia Law Review* 108, no. 97 (2005–2006).

Lindgren, K. "Maternal Fetal Conflict. Court-Ordered Cesarean Section." *Journal of Obstetric, Gynecologic, and Neonatal Nursing* 25, no. 8 (October 1996): 653–56.

"Safe Prevention of the Primary Cesarean Delivery." American Congress of Obstetricians and Gynecologists and the Society for Maternal-Fetal Medicine, March 2014.

Reflection #33

Cohen, Elizabeth. "Surrogate Offered $10,000 to Abort Baby." CNN.com, March 6, 2013.

Bains, Inderdeep. "'I Don't Want a Dribbling Cabbage for a Daughter': What Mother Told Her Surrogate Before Rejecting Disabled Baby Girl." *Daily Mail*, August 26, 2014.

Reflection #34

Buck v. Bell, 274 U.S. 200 (1927).

Denekens, Joke P. M., Herman Nys, and Hugo Stuer. "Sterilisation of Incompetent Mentally Handicapped Persons: A Model for Decision Making." *Journal of Medical Ethics* 25, no. 3 (June 1999): 237–41.

Gould, Stephen Jay. "Carrie Buck's Daughter." *Natural History*, July 1984.

Paul, Diane B. *Controlling Human Heredity: 1865 to the Present*. Atlantic Highlands, NJ: Humanities Press, 1995.

Reflection #35

Brooks, Robert. "'Asia's Missing Women' as a Problem in Applied Evolutionary Psychology?" *Evolutionary Psychology* 10, no. 5 (2012): 910–25.

Cox, David. "Hong Kong's Troubling Shortage of Men." *Atlantic*, December 2, 2013.

Hudson, Valerie M., and Andrea M. den Boer. *Bare Branches: The Security Implications of Asia's Surplus Male Population*. Cambridge, MA: MIT Press, 2015.

Oster, Emily. "Hepatitis B and the Case of the Missing Women." *Journal of Political Economy* 113, no. 6 (December 2005): 1163–1216.

Sen, Amartya . "More Than 100 Million Women Are Missing," *New York Review of Books*, December 20, 1990.

Sidhu, Jasmeet. "How to Buy a Daughter." *Slate*, September 14, 2012.

Reflection #36

Appel, Jacob M. "Physicians, 'Wrongful Life' and the Constitution." *Medicine and Health Rhode Island* 87, no. 2 (2004): 55–58.

Hensel, Wendy Fritzen. "The Disabling Impact of Wrongful Birth and Wrongful Life Actions." 40 *Harvard Civil Rights-Civil Liberties Law Review* 40 (2005): 141.

Latson, Jennifer. "How an Abortion-Clinic Shooting Led to a 'Wrongful Life' Lawsuit." *Time*, December 30, 2014.

Reflection #37

Caulfield, Timothy. "Human Cloning Laws, Human Dignity and the Poverty of the Policy Making Dialogue." *BMC Medical Ethics* 4, no. 3 (2003).

Church, George M. *Regenesis: How Synthetic Biology Will Reinvent Nature and Ourselves*. New York: Basic Books, 2014.

Kass, Leon R. "The Wisdom of Repugnance." *New Republic*, June 2, 1997.

———. "Preventing a Brave New World: Why We Should Ban Human Cloning Now." *New Republic*, May 21, 2001.

Savulescu, Julian. "How Will History Judge Cloning?" *Times Higher Education*, May 6, 2005.

Watson, James. "Moving toward a Clonal Man: Is This What We Want?" *Atlantic Monthly*, May 1971.

Reflection #38

Hughes, Virginia. "Return of the Neanderthals: Should Scientists Seek to Clone Our Ancient Hominid Cousins?" *National Geographic News*, March 6, 2013.

"Interview with George Church: Can Neanderthals Be Brought Back from the Dead?" *Spiegel Online*, January 18, 2013.

Smith, Rebecca. "'I Can Create Neanderthal Baby, I Just Need Willing Woman.'" *Telegraph*, January 20, 2013.

Reflection #39

Curry, Tyler. "Texas Dads Denied Surrogacy Services Because of Marriage Discrimination." Advocate.com, January 14, 2015.

Egelko, Bob. "Doctors Can't Use Bias to Deny Gays Treatment." *San Francisco Gate*, August 19, 2008.

North Coast Women's Care Medical Group vs. Superior Court, 44 Cal. 4th 1145 (2008).

Reflection #40

Hackler, Chris. "Ethical, Legal and Policy Issues in Management of Fetal Alcohol Spectrum Disorder." *Journal of the Arkansas Medical Society* 108, no. 6 (November 2011): 123–24.

Seamark, Michael. "The American Woman Who Wants to 'Bribe' UK Heroin Users with £200 to Have Vasectomies." *Daily Mail*, October 19, 2010.

Vega, Cecilia M. "Sterilization Offer to Addicts Reopens Ethics Issue." *New York Times*, January 6, 2003.

Reflection #41

Finigan, Michael W, Shannon M. Carey, and Anton Cox. *Impact of a Mature Drug Court over 10 Years of Operation: Recidivism and Costs*, July 2007.

Gentilello, L. M., F. P. Rivara, D. M. Donovan, G. J. Jurkovich, E. Daranciang, C. W. Dunn, A. Villaveces, M. Copass, and R. R. Ries. "Alcohol Interventions in a Trauma Center as a Means of Reducing the Risk of Injury Recurrence." *Annals of Surgery* 230, no. 4 (October 1999): 473.

Sutton, Malcolm. "NT Move to Mandatory Alcohol Rehabilitation Sparks Controversy." *Guardian*, June 30, 2013.

Szalavitz, Maia. "How America Overdosed on Drug Courts." *Pacific Standard*, May 18, 2015.

Reflection #42

"Andrew Speaker, Quarantined for Tuberculosis in 2007, Sues CDC for Invasion of Privacy." Associated Press, April 30, 2009.

Leavitt, Judith Walzer. *Typhoid Mary: Captive to the Public's Health.* Boston: Beacon Press, 1996.

Wynia, M. K. "Ethics and Public Health Emergencies: Restrictions on Liberty." *American Journal of Bioethics* 7, no. 2 (February 2007): 1–5.

Reflection #43

Halbfinger, David M. "Police Dragnets for DNA Tests Draw Criticism." *New York Times*, January 4, 2003.

Povoledo, Elisabetta. "In Search for Killer, DNA Sweep Exposes Intimate Family Secrets in Italy." *New York Times*, July 26, 2014.

Reflection #44

Carmichael, Mary. "Newborn Screening: A Spot of Trouble." *Nature* 475 (July 13, 2011): 156–58.

Gabler, Ellen. "Privacy Issues Stall Newborn Screening Bill in U.S. Senate." *Journal Sentinel*, November 29, 2014.

Greenfieldboyce, Nell. "Screening Newborns for Disease Can Leave Families in Limbo." *Health News Florida*, December 23, 2013.

Hazzazi, Hussain, and Ayman Al-Saidalani. "165,000 Engagements End Due to 'Genetic Incompatibilities.'" *Saudi Gazette*, March 24, 2015.

Reflection #45

Appel, Jacob M. "Rethinking Force-Feeding: Legal and Ethical Aspects of Physician Participation in the Termination of Hunger Strikes in American Prisons." *Public Affairs Quarterly* 26, no. 4 (October 2012): 313–35.

Greenberg, Joel K. "Hunger Striking Prisoners: The Constitutionality of Force-Feeding." *Fordham Law Review* 51, no. 4 (March 1983): 747–70.

Neumann, Ann. "Guantánamo Is Not an Anomaly—Prisoners in the US Are Force-Fed Every Day." *Common Dreams*, May 6, 2013.

Reflection #46

"Doctor 'Fires' Patients Who Refuse to Vaccinate Their Kids." Associated Press, January 30, 2015.

Dominus, Susan. "The Crash and Burn of an Autism Guru." *New York Times Magazine*, April 20, 2011.

Mejia, Brittny. "Doctors Turning Away Unvaccinated Children." *Los Angeles Times*, February 11, 2015.

Reflection #47

Cain, John. "Nonconsensual Surgery: The Unkindest Cut of All." *Notre Dame Law Review* 53, no. 2 (1977): 291.

Gitles, Jay A. "Reasonableness of Surgical Intrusions—Fourth Amendment: Winston v. Lee, 105 S. Ct. 1611." *Journal of Criminal Law and Criminology* 76, no. 4 (1985): 972.

Minton, Michael B. "Criminal Procedure—Surgical Removal of Evidence—United States v. Crowder." *Missouri Law Review* 43 (1978).

Winston v. Lee, 470 U.S. 753 (1985).

Reflection #48

Angell, Marcia. "The Ethics of Clinical Research in the Third World." *New England Journal of Medicine* 337, no. 12 (September 18, 1997): 847–49.

Lurie, Peter, and Sidney M. Wolfe. "Unethical Trials of Interventions to Reduce Perinatal Transmission of the Human Immunodeficiency Virus in Developing Countries." *New England Journal of Medicine* 337, no. 12 (September 18, 1997): 853–56.

Rothman, David J. "The Shame of Medical Research." *New York Review of Books*, November 30, 2000.

Reflection #49

Appelbaum, P. S., L. H. Roth, and C. Lidz. "The Therapeutic Misconception: Informed Consent in Psychiatric Research." *International Journal of Law and Psychiatry* 5, no. 3–4 (1982): 319–29.

Institutional Review Board Guidebook, US Department of Health and Human Services, 1993.

Kolata, Gina. "What to Tell the Patients after a Trial Goes Awry." *New York Times*, August 23, 2010.

Lidz, C. W., and P. S. Appelbaum. "The Therapeutic Misconception: Problems and Solutions." *Medical Care* 40, no. 9 Suppl (September 2002): V55–63.

Rosenthal, Elisabeth. "When Drug Trials Go Horribly Wrong." *New York Times*, April 7, 2006.

Woods, Simon, Lynn E. Hagger, and Pauline Mccormack. "Therapeutic Misconception: Hope, Trust and Misconception in Paediatric Research." *Health Care Analysis* 22, no. 1 (February 2012).

Reflection #50

Fels, Anna. "Should We All Take a Bit of Lithium?" *New York Times*, September 13, 2014.

Kapusta, N. D., N. Mossaheb, E. Etzersdorfer, G. Hlavin, K. Thau, M. Willeit, N. Praschak-Rieder, G. Sonneck, and K. Leithner-Dziubas. "Lithium in Drinking Water and Suicide Mortality." *British Journal of Psychiatry* 198, no. 5 (May 2011): 346–50.

Schrauzer, G. N., and K. P. Shrestha. "Lithium in Drinking Water and the Incidences of Crimes, Suicides, and Arrests Related to Drug Addictions." *Biological Trace Element Research* 25, no. 2 (May 1990): 105–13.

Reflection #51

Bradshaw v. Daniel 854 S.W.2d 865 (Tenn. 1993).

King, Michelle R. "Physician Duty to Warn a Patient's Offspring of Hereditary Genetic Defects: Balancing the Patient's Right to Confidentiality Against the Family Member's Right to Know—Can or Should Tarasoff Apply?" *Quinnipiac Health Law Journal* 4, no. 1 (2000): 1–38.

Schleiter, Kristin E. "A Physician's Duty to Warn Third Parties of Hereditary Risk." *AMA Journal of Ethics* 11, no. 9 (September 2009): 697–700.

Sudell, Andrea. "To Tell or Not to Tell: The Scope of Physician-Patient Confidentiality When Relatives Are At Risk of Genetic Disease." *Journal of Contemporary Health Law & Policy* 18, no. 1 (Winter 2001): 273.

Reflection #52

Abbott, Alison. "Regulations Proposed for Animal–Human Chimaeras." *Nature* 475 (July 2011).

Appel, Jacob M. "The Monster's Laws: A Legal History of Chimera Research." *GeneWatch* 19, no. 2 (March–April 2006): 12–16.

Greely, Henry T., Mildred K. Cho, Linda F. Hogle, and Debra M. Satz. "Thinking About the Human Neuron Mouse." *American Journal of Bioethics* 7, no. 5 (May 2007): 27–40.

Hilts, Philip J. "The Business of Manipulating Life." *Washington Post*, April 21, 1987.

Karpowicz, P., C. B. Cohen, and D. van der Kooy. "Developing Human-Nonhuman Chimeras in Human Stem Cell Research: Ethical Issues and Boundaries." *Kennedy Institute of Ethics Journal* 15, no. 2 (June 2005): 107–34.

Reflection #53

"Bahrain's Doctors: Harsh Treatment." *Economist*, January 28, 2014.

Brinkley, Joel. "Dictators Spurn Their Nations' Health Care." *San Francisco Gate*, September 1, 2012.

Bueno de Mesquita, Bruce, and Alastair Smith. "In Sickness and in Health: Why Leaders Keep Their Illnesses Secret." *Foreign Policy*, September 18, 2012.

Owen, David. "Diseased, Demented, Depressed: Serious Illness in Heads of State." *QJM* 96, no. 5 (May 1, 2003): 325–36.

Reflection #54

Green, Robert C., Denise Lautenbach, and Amy L. McGuire. "GINA, Genetic Discrimination, and Genomic Medicine." *New England Journal of Medicine* 372 (January 29, 2015): 397–99.

Sullivan, Andrew. "Promotion of the Fittest." *New York Times*, July 23, 2000.

Reflection #55

Chen, Frederick M., George E. Fryer Jr., Robert L. Phillips, Elisabeth Wilson, and Donald E. Pathman. "Patients' Beliefs about Racism, Preferences for Physician Race, and Satisfaction with Care." *Annals of Family Medicine* 3, no. 2 (2005): 138–43.

Johnson, Amy M., Peter F. Schnatz, Anita M. Kelsey, and Christine M. Ohannessian. "Do Women Prefer Care from Female or Male Obstetrician-Gynecologists? A Study of Patient Gender Preference." *Journal of the American Osteopathic Association* 105 (August 2005): 369–79.

Paul-Emile, Kimani. "Patient Racial Preferences and the Medical Culture of Accommodation." *UCLA Law Review* 60 (2012).

Waseem, Muhammad, and Aaron K. Miller. "Patient Requests for a Male or Female Physician." *AMA Journal of Ethics* 10, no. 7 (July 2008): 429–33.

Reflection #56

McCabe, Mary S., William A. Wood, and Richard M. Goldberg. "When the Family Requests Withholding the Diagnosis: Who Owns the Truth?" *Journal of Oncology Practice* 6, no. 2 (March 2010): 94–96.

Oken, Donald. "What to Tell Cancer Patients: A Study of Medical Attitudes." *JAMA* 175, no. 13 (1961): 1120–28.

Reflection #57

Appelbaum, P. S., and T. Grisso. "Assessing Patients' Capacities to Consent to Treatment." *New England Journal of Medicine* 319, no. 25 (December 22, 1988): 1635–38.

Fraser, Caroline. "Suffering Children and the Christian Science Church." *Atlantic Monthly*, April 1995.

Perry, Candace Lyn, Maria Isabel Lapid, and Jarrett W. Richardson. "Ethical Dilemmas with an Elderly Christian Scientist." *Annals of Long-Term Care* 15, no. 3 (March 2007): 29–34.

Reflection #58

Armour, Stephanie. "U.S. Recovers $3.3 Billion in Federal Health-Care Fraud." *Wall Street Journal*, March 19, 2015.

Reflection #59

Cohen, Steven B. "The Concentration of Health Care Expenditures and Related Expenses for Costly Medical Conditions, 2012." Medical Expenditure Panel Survey, October 2014.

Gawande, Atul. "The Hot Spotters: Can We Lower Medical Costs by Giving the Neediest Patients Better Care?" *New Yorker*, January 24, 2011.

Winslow, Ron. "One Patient, 34 Days in the Hospital, $7,000 Syringes and a $5.2 Million Bill." *Wall Street Journal*, August 2, 2001.

Reflection #60

"Allocation of Ventilators in an Influenza Pandemic: Planning Document." Draft for Public Comment, New York State, March 15, 2007.

Appel, Jacob M. "The Coming Ethical Crisis: Oxygen Rationing." *Huffington Post*, July 28, 2009.

Dean, Cornelia. "Guidelines for Epidemics: Who Gets a Ventilator?" *New York Times*, March 25, 2008.

Reflection #61

Berenson, Alex. "A Cancer Drug Shows Promise, at a Price That Many Can't Pay." *New York Times*, February 15, 2006.

Grewal, David Singh, and Amy Kapczynski. "Let India Make Cheap Drugs." *New York Times*, December 11, 2014.

McNeil Jr., Donald G. "Selling Cheap 'Generic' Drugs, India's Copycats Irk Industry." *New York Times*, December 1, 2000.

Ornstein, Charles. "New Hepatitis C Drugs Are Costing Medicare Billions." *Washington Post*, March 29, 2015.

Ram, Prabhu. "India's New 'TRIPs-Compliant' Patent Regime: Between Drug Patents and the Right to Health." *Chicago-Kent Journal of Intellectual Property* 5, no. 2 (2006).

Reflection #62

Coker, Hillary Crosley. "Canadian Sperm Bank Finally Decides Race Mixing Is Okay." *Jezebel*, July 29, 2014.

Goff, Keli. "The Real Problem with Sperm Banks." *Daily Beast*, October 7, 2014.

Rodriguez, Meredith. "Lawsuit: Wrong Sperm Delivered to Lesbian Couple." *Chicago Tribune*, October 1, 2014.

Sheridan, Michael. "World's Biggest Sperm Bank, Cryos, Tells Redheads: We Don't Want Your Semen." *Daily News*, September 18, 2011.

"Sperm Bank Is For Whites Only—Spokane Effort Reportedly Funded by Tycoon." Associated Press, August 6, 1996.

Reflection #63

Casey, Liam. "North Bay Hospital to Offer Co-Ed Hospital Rooms." *Star*, August 31, 2010.

Miner, John. "Shared Room Sparks Rage Outrage." *London Free Press*, June 17, 2010.

Reflection #64

Anderson, Elizabeth. "Nearly Half of Employers 'Unlikely' to Hire Overweight Workers." *Telegraph*, April 8, 2015.

Cawley, John., and Chad Meyerhoefer. "The Medical Care Costs of Obesity: An Instrumental Variables Approach." *Journal of Health Economics* 31, no. 1 (January 2012): 219–230.

Holt, Mytheos. "Texas Hospital Bans Overweight Employees." *Blaze*, April 4, 2012.

Koch, Wendy. "Workplaces Ban Not Only Smoking, but Smokers Themselves." *USA Today*, January 6, 2102.

Sulzberger, A. G. "Hospitals Shift Smoking Bans to Smoker Ban." *New York Times*, February 10, 2011.

Reflection #65

Appel, Jacob M., and Joseph H. Friedman. "Genetic Markers and the Majority's Right Not to Know." *Movement Disorders* 19, no. 1 (January 2004): 113–14.

Howe, Edmund G. "Ethical Issues in Diagnosing and Treating Alzheimer Disease." *Psychiatry* 3, no. 5 (May 2006): 43–53.

Nyholt, Dale R., Chang-En Yu, and Peter M. Visscher. "On Jim Watson's APOE Status: Genetic Information is Hard to Hide." *European Journal of Human Genetics* 17, no. 2 (February 2009): 147–49.

Pinker, Steven. "My Genome, My Self." *New York Times Magazine*, January 7, 2009.

Reflection #66

Leonhardt, David. "Health Care Rationing Rhetoric Overlooks Reality." *New York Times*, June 17, 2009.

Perry, Philip A., and Timothy Hotze. "Oregon's Experiment with Prioritizing Public Health Care Services." *AMA Journal of Ethics* 13, no. 3 (April 2011): 241–47.

Singer, Peter. "Why We Must Ration Health Care." *New York Times*, July 15, 2009.

Thurow, Lester Carl. "Learning to Say No." *New England Journal of Medicine* 311 (December 13, 1984): 1569–72.

Reflection #67

Appel, Jacob M. "When the Boss Turns Pusher: A Proposal for Employee Protections in the Age of Cosmetic Neurology." *Journal of Medical Ethics* 34, no. 8 (2008).

Cadwalladr, Carole. "Students Used to Take Drugs to Get High. Now They Take Them to Get Higher Grades." *Guardian*, February 14, 2015.

Chatterjee, Anjan. "Cosmetic Neurology and Cosmetic Surgery: Parallels, Predictions, and Challenges." *Cambridge Quarterly of Healthcare Ethics* 16, no. 2 (April 2007): 129–37.

Reflection #68

Appelbaum, Paul S. "Law and Psychiatry: Psychiatric Advance Directives and the Treatment of Committed Patients." *Psychiatric Services* 55, no. 7 (July 2004): 751–63.

Hargrave v. Vermont, 340 F. 3d 27 (2nd Cir. 2003).

Swanson, Jeffrey W., S. Van McCrary, Marvin S. Swartz, Eric B. Elbogen, and Richard A. Van Dorn. "Superseding Psychiatric Advance Directives: Ethical and Legal Considerations," *Journal of the American Academy of Psychiatry and the Law* 34, no. 3 (September 2006): 385–94.

Zelle, Heather, Kathleen Kemp, and Richard J. Bonnie. "Advance Directives for Mental Health Care: Innovation in Law, Policy, and Practice." *Psychiatric Services* 66, no. 1 (January 2015): 7–9.

Reflection #69

Appel, Jacob M. "Health 'Insurance': A Criminal Enterprise." *Huffington Post*, March 18, 2010.

Beiser, E. N. "The Emperor's New Scrubs: Thoughts about Health Care Reform." *Rhode Island Medical Journal* 77, no. 9 (September 1994): 304–6.

Williams, Geoff. "How Risky Hobbies Can Raise Your Insurance Rates." *US News & World Report*, April 16, 2013.

Reflection #70

Engber, Daniel. "Naughty Nursing Homes: Is It Time to Let the Elderly Have More Sex?" *Slate*, September 27, 2007.

Gray, Eliza. "Why Nursing Homes Need to Have Sex Policies." *Time*, April 23, 2015.

Leys, Tony. "Husband Acquitted of Nursing Home Sex-Abuse Charge." *Des Moines Register*, April 22, 2015.

Zernike, Kate. "Love in the Time of Dementia." *New York Times*, November 18, 2007.

Reflection #71

Appel, Jacob M. "Defining Death: When Physicians and Families Differ." *Journal of Medical Ethics* 31, no. 11 (2005): 641–42.

Labbé-DeBose, Theola, David Brown, and Keith L. Alexander. "Jewish Law's Meaning of Death Nears Court Fight." *Washington Post*, November 7, 2008.

Reflection #72

Holt, Jim. "Euthanasia for Babies?" *New York Times Magazine*, July 10, 2005.

Verhagen, A. A. E., and P. J. J. Sauer. "End-of-Life Decisions in Newborns: An Approach from the Netherlands." *Pediatrics* 116, no. 3 (September 2005): 736–39.

Reflection #73

Saunders, Laura. "Rich Cling to Life to Beat Tax Man." *Wall Street Journal*, December 30, 2009.

Reflection #74

Berg, Jessica Wilen. "Grave Secrets: Legal and Ethical Analysis of Postmortem Confidentiality." *Connecticut Law Review* 34 (2001): 81.

Bongers, L. M. "Disclosure of Medical Data to Relatives after the Patient's Death: Recent Legal Developments with Respect to Relatives' Entitlements in the Netherlands." *European Journal of Health Law* 18, no. 3 (May 2011): 255–75.

Choong, Kartina Aisha, Mifsud Bonnici, and Jeanne Pia. "Posthumous Medical Confidentiality: The Public Interest Conundrum." *European Journal of Comparative Law and Governance* 1, no. 2 (2014): 106–19.

Reflection #75

Appel, Jacob M. "A Duty to Kill? A Duty to Die? Rethinking the Euthanasia Controversy of 1906." *Bulletin of The History of Medicine* 78, no. 3 (Fall 2004): 610–34.

Bailey, Ryan. "The Case of Dr. Anna Pou: Physician Liability in Emergency Situations." *AMA Journal of Ethics* 12, no. 9 (September 2010): 726–30.

Drew, Christopher, and Sheila Dewan. "Louisiana Doctor Said to Have Faced Chaos." *New York Times*, July 20, 2006.

Fink, Sheri. "The Deadly Choices at Memorial." *New York Times Magazine*, August 25, 2009.

Schaffer, Amanda. "The Moral Dilemmas of Doctors during Disaster." *New Yorker*, September 12, 2013.

Reflection #76

Lerner, Barron H. "In a Wife's Request at Her Husband's Deathbed, Ethics Are an Issue." *New York Times*, September 7, 2004.

Myers, Russell. "I'll Give Birth to My Dead Daughter's Baby: World First as Mum Uses Frozen Eggs for Own Grandchild." *Mirror*, May 8, 2015.

Orr, R. D., and M. Siegler. "Is Posthumous Semen Retrieval Ethically Permissible?" *Journal of Medical Ethics* 28, no. 5 (October 2002): 299–302.

Reflection #77

Belluck, Pam. "Even as Doctors Say Enough, Families Fight to Prolong Life." *New York Times*, March 27, 2005.

Dzielak, Robert J. "Physicians Lose the Tug of War to Pull the Plug: The Debate about Continued Futile Medical Care." *John Marshall Law School Law Review* 28, no. 3 (Spring 1995).

Larimer, Sarah. "Midwest Miracle: Woman Woke Up Hours Before She Was Going to Be Taken Off Life Support." *Washington Post*, February 2, 2015.

Laytner, Ron. "Mrs Rip Van Winkle's Love Story Finally Ends." *Jamaica Observer*, November 23, 2003.

Reflection #78

Eversley, Melanie. "Tenn. Funeral Home Allegedly Mixes Up Corpses." *USA Today*, February 17, 2010.

Fried, Richard G., and Clifford Perlis. "'Therapeutic Privilege: If, When, and How to Lie to Patients." In *Dermatoethics: Contemporary Ethics and Professionalism in Dermatology*, 33–36. New York: Springer, 2011.

Griffith, Dorsey. "Baby's Corpse Mistakenly Buried with Twins." *Sacramento Bee*, May 24, 2006.

Lynn, Guy. "Exhumation after Wrong Bodies Buried in Hospital Mix-Up." BBC News, July 4, 2011.

Richard, Claude, Yvette Lajeunesse, and Marie-Thérèse Lussier. "Therapeutic Privilege: Between the Ethics of Lying and the Practice of Truth." *Journal of Medical Ethics* 36, no. 6 (June 2010): 353–57.

Reflection #79

Davies, Madlen. "Builder Who Had All Four Limbs Amputated after 'Flu' Turned Out to Be a Flesh-Eating Bug Is Finally Able to Walk Again Thanks to Prosthetic Legs." *Daily Mail*, April 20, 2015.

Gilmore, Annie. "Sanctity of Life Versus Quality of Life—the Continuing Debate." *Canadian Medical Association Journal* 130, no. 2 (January 15, 1984): 180–81.

O'Connor, C. M. "Statutory Surrogate Consent Provisions: A Review and Analysis." *Mental and Physical Disability Law Reporter* 20 (1996): 128–38.

Wynn, Shana. "Decisions by Surrogates: An Overview of Surrogate Consent Laws in the United States." *Bifocal* 36, no. 1 (September–October 2014): 10–14.